CW00819766

THEY LABOUR MIGHTILY

SEA HARVEST
Skipper J. R. Storr, D.S.M.

Frontispiece]

THEY LABOUR MIGHTILY

A TALE OF INSHORE FISHING
IN WAR AND PEACE

BY

DORA M. WALKER

WITH

A FOREWORD

BY

CHARLES W. DOMVILLE-FIFE

LONDON
A. BROWN & SONS, LIMITED
32 BROOKE STREET, HOLBORN, E.C.1.
AND AT HULL
1947

First published in 1947 by
A. Brown and Sons Ltd

This new edition published
2002 by
Caedmon of Whibty
128 Upgang Lane
Whitby

ISBN 0905355 54 7

Printed and bound by
Smith Settle
Gateway Drive, Yeadon LS19 7XY

DEDICATED TO A GREAT FELLOWSHIP

THE

" BRETHREN OF THE COAST "

PREFACE

I GRATEFULLY acknowledge the permission given by Mr. Charles Domville-Fife, editor of the *Seagoer* to re-publish articles on " Tunny Hunting," " A Coble's Log," and " Storm."

I also thank Kemsley Newspapers Ltd. for permission to use two photographs of the *Good Faith* (Series 70768 A and B), and Doran Bros., Whitby, for one photograph of the motor keel-boat *Pilot Me*.

" Crabs, 1932," appeared first in the *Dewsbury Reporter* in the Autumn of 1932 and " Lines at Christmas " the next Winter.

A censored edition of " Fishermen of England " was given in a broadcast in June, 1940.

The whole are now put together, with some additions, not as a " history," but as a " sketch " of life on the quayside and some of the inshore grounds of the North Sea between the years 1931 and the present date.

DORA M. WALKER.

CONTENTS

LIST OF PLATES

LIST OF PLATES xiii

FOREWORD

THERE is only one justification for a foreword between the title page and the beginning of any story. It is that the writer has something to say which may, perhaps, intensify the reader's interest by furthering the purpose for which the book is written. Dora Walker is not only a practical " seaman " who skippers her own boat in calm and storm, in summer and winter, in the North Sea, but she also writes graphically and with an unbounded enthusiasm for those hardy and courageous men who labour mightily in the stormy seas on Britain's eastern frontier.

I suggest to all those into whose hands this book may fall that it is not *just* an account of inshore fishing off the Yorkshire coast, nor is it exclusively of local or merely passing interest. It is a vivid picture of one aspect of the great and valuable harvest of the sea. It is a study of a breed of seamen known for their skill and hardy courage in both peace and war. When such men cease to exist then England—and the Royal Navy who knows and values them so highly—will be the poorer for their passing. Read it, then, not only as an interesting narrative, but also as a fragment—a valuable fragment in the years to come—of our glorious maritime history.

The fishermen of the East Coast, from Dover to the Shetlands, have for centuries supplied the major portion of the sea food of the people of the British Isles ; and in time of war these men have contributed handsomely to the trained and experienced personnel of the Royal Navy and its Reserves. Their deeds have in the past been recorded and handed down for the encouragement of succeeding generations by just such plain tales of the sea as are recorded in this first-hand study of a fishing port with its people and their work in great waters in times of peace and during the greatest war in all history—a war that literally was on their front doorstep.

Born and bred within sight and sound of the North Sea, I have sailed its waters from the Arctic ice to the Straits of Dover in command of ships of the Royal Navy with men from this coast as shipmates. My earliest recollections include a mental picture of a wild January night, blazing barrels of tar throwing a lurid light on a raging sea and a lifeboat plunging into the swirling foam. My first sea fight I saw through a telescope from a cliff top. Coastguards from a yawl with drawn cutlasses were boarding a foreign fishing vessel poaching close inshore and fighting its crew who were armed with fish knives and hatchets. In later years it was Jutland and after.

I count it an honour, therefore, to add this inadequate little foreword to what I know to be the Author's main objective—the publication of a true picture which will do justice to those battling daily with the North Sea for a hard-won living and who have been called upon for anything up to ten years' service with the Fleets at war during the lifetime of one generation.

CHARLES W. DOMVILLE-FIFE.

London, 1946.

PART ONE

FISHING OUT OF WHITBY
1932—1939

WHITBY FLEET BEFORE THE WAR
1938-1939
LIST OF COBLES AND KEEL-BOATS AND THEIR CREWS

KEEL-BOATS	SKIPPER	CREW
Pilot Me	JOHN ROBERT STORR, D.S.M.	W. STORR, M. STORR, R. STORR, A. NOBLE
Success	MAT. LEADLEY	J. LEADLEY, B. NOBLE, F. RUSSEL, W. RICHARDSON
Progress	MAT. WINSPEAR	H. WINSPEAR, A. RICHARDSON, ROB HANSELL
Provider	JOHN JAMES STORR	C. RUSSEL, D. NOBLE, R. HARLAND
Endeavour	T. HUTCHINSON	M. HUTCHINSON, J. W. STORRY, J. RICHARDSON
Galilee	EDWARD VERRILL	J. THEAKER, R. THEAKER, JOS. DUKE
Venus	JAMES COLE	A. COLE, J. COLE, E. VERRILL
Prosperity	J. DRYDEN	W. DRYDEN, W. KELLY, R. FORDEN, H. RICHARDSON
Easter Morn	HENRY DUKE	E. DUKE, G. DUKE, T. STORM

COBLES	COX AND CREW
Royal Empire	T. WALE, J. WALE, W. SMITH
Silver Line	C. EGLON, C. EGLON (JUN.), W. J. WINSPEAR, L. VASEY
Comrades	J. HARRISON, M. LEADLEY, G. LEADLEY, J. HEBDEN
Good Faith	D. M. WALKER, LAURENCE MIRFIELD
Ramleh	D. HARLAND, T. HARLAND, J. NOBLE
Brighter Hope	J. MIRFIELD, H. MIRFIELD, J. MIRFIELD (JUN.)
Margaret	R. WALKER, R. WALKER (JUN.), J. WALKER
Mayflower	G. MIRFIELD, G. MIRFIELD (JUN.), A. MIRFIELD
Enterprize	R. ALLEN, R. ALLEN (JUN.), W. ALLEN
June and Anne	H. RICHARDSON, C. WALE, W. ELDERS
Guide Me	J. THEAKER, W. THEAKER, S. PEARL
Lady Morris	J. WINSPEAR, J. WINSPEAR (JUN.)
True Love	R. HARLAND, R. HARLAND (JUN.), J. R DRYDEN
Sarah	J. NOBLE, R. NOBLE, J. WOOD
Iris	J. WOOD, W. WINSPEAR
Helena	J. DOUGLAS, R. DOUGLAS

CHAPTER I

"CRABS, 1932"

THIS is a brief account of ships and men, written during fifteen years of Inshore Fishing, including a year of war.

From childhood I had yearned to own a Whitby coble and fish it, and as it often happens that, when you intensely desire a thing, you get it—at a price!—I got my coble.

The price was a long spell of ill-health necessitating sea air. The outcome of doctor's orders was a house in Whitby and the opportunity to get a boat built, and to spend the interim of waiting in learning how to work gear, and boat. I was exceedingly lucky in having a friend willing to take the risk of a woman aboard his ship. He was at an age when a sailing coble, with the necessity of long spells at the oars, can be a heavy burden. My "apprentice fee," as third hand or "fisherman's" boy for twelve months, was a Kelvin petrol engine. It was duly installed.

In June, 1932, the *Helena* went crabbing. Our day's work began at 4-30 a.m. With the mist of the night still shrouding the waterside, there was something monstrous about the appearance of the boats. They looked like prehistoric creatures that had crept in overnight! Actually their deformity was due to stacks of crab pots in ordered piles, with quantities of rope "tows" and two cork buoys with flags attached : "enders" as they are named. There hardly seemed room for the three of us besides all the gear, but we crowded in. The cox told me it would be my job to take the crabs out of the pots after the first haul. These "pots" resembled rat-traps. They had a frame of tarred netting stretched over four, or three, hoops of hazel secured to a wood base, ballasted with iron. The crab made his entry through a funnel in the mesh with a drop end that landed him safely on the bottom, a prisoner—for though a great climber, he is unable to jump.

He had to be removed through a door in the mesh fastened with twine. The bait, fish heads and fillets (or gurnets when procurable) was inserted between two perpendicular pieces of twine wedged tight by a sliding knot. I anxiously studied these as the coble ran down the coast about half a mile from the rocky shore.

The rim of the sun rose suddenly out of the sea; as we reached our ground, the cox barked an order, and energy broke loose. Over went the "ender" or marking buoy, with its tall flag; fifty to sixty fathoms of tow line followed, and then, attached to this by short lengths of rope at equal intervals, the crab pots were speeded on their way by the "second," who lifted them from the stack and cast them overboard. Sometimes, as the boat moved on its course, the "tow" outpaced him, and a pot escaped his hands, and jumped like a live thing into the sea. Something stirred by my feet. "Keep your feet clear of that tow," yelled the cox, and I withdrew them quickly from the moving coil. "That was how young 'Banger' nearly lost his life," he warned me. "He got a coil round his leg, and was dragged over the side to the bottom. They had to fix the tow to the winch and haul him inboard that way. They were nearly too late."

I had reason to remember that story in later days aboard my own boat, when my engineer got caught

SHOOTING POTS
Mat Storr on *Pilot Me*

HAULING IN THE TOW
L. Mirfield and R. Harland (Skipper) aboard *Flying Spray*

[*facing page* 4

COX STOWING POTS
Chief Pilot Jack Douglas

TAKING OUT THE CRABS
William Theaker

in the same way. He had his knee over the gunwale before I managed to relax the strain by throwing the engine hard astern, at great risk of the propeller running over the tow.

When the last pot had sunk to the sea floor, and the coils of the end tow had followed it, the cox lifted the second buoy over the side looking landwards. " ' Nab's on, ' and a bunch of trees over Sandsend water tower." Then for my benefit : " Those are the marks to pick the buoy up by to-morrow."

But by " to-morrow " there were no marks to be seen. As we crept through the fog the compass indicated our direction and a watch in the cox's hand the distance travelled. We were too near shore to be troubled by the steamers' warning sirens, but we listened with strained attention to the sound of breaking seas. A lightening of the strain, more than any word, told me that the buoy was close at hand. I put the engine out of gear as the " Second " plunged the boathook overside to retrieve the buoy. My work that day was first to lift in the pots as they rose to the surface in response to the labours of the man with the tow (small cobles had not yet achieved mechanical " pot haulers "). Then, taking out the crabs, to pass the pots on to the " Second " to rebait, fasten up, and stow. Bad stowage can cause an accident similar to " Banger's," when the pots come to be " shot " again ; a " granny " knot on a door can occasion delay, that results in the " tow " becoming fast in the rocks beneath ! That entails awkward manœuvring with possibly lost pots, a broken tow line, or worse still, a tow fast in the propeller, and another kind of " tow " the only way of getting home ! Because of this team-work and interdependence, there is developed among the crews a sense of comradeship that is the life and soul of fishing. Bad work does not pay. It may harm your fellow—or drown you, and your skill enhances the success of all!

So I found myself joyfully lifting aboard heavy pots that had six crabs in; or carefully extracting a viciously snapping lobster (their equal in value). For while crabs often bring only three-half-pence in slack times, a lobster seldom fetches less than sixpence. And I found myself joying and grieving with the fortune of the boat.

But that fortune is dependent on more than a good haul.

At the Fish Market each skipper or crew stands by his catch. The Auctioneer, noting down the names of each boat with a friendly grin, starts crying the price. Competition begins. "How many buyers are there? Is Sutton here?" So much depends on it.

The business of the buyers is concerned with markets beyond our own—on trawlers that sometimes glut other ports—on demand as well as supply. But to each skipper and crew the Auction is the completion of a day's work.

If the weather has allowed them to work their gear and fetch it in, if the catch is good, there is still this last gamble. Will the price to-day be high or low?

I watched the men's faces as the crabs were knocked down at ten shillings a box, and sighed with relief. A box held fifty odd. The price was up!

CITY OF LEEDS BRINGING IN THE POTS
Cox Dave Harland

KEEL-BOAT UNLOADING POTS
Pilot Me   [*facing page* 6

TWO LOBSTERS IN A POT
Robert Harland and L. Mirfield

MENDING POTS AFTER A STORM

THE SAND-BAR AT THE HARBOUR MOUTH

Leaving the silent Quay
Before the Dawn,
All weather-worn
The boats put out to sea,
Seeking the Fishing-Ground
North-Eastward bound.

Labour and Luck and skill
The long hours fill,
While deft hands clear
And work intricate gear
Till the wet, slithering hoard
Piles up aboard.

But now the heaving sea
Grows mightily.
The Skipper's eye
Scanning the Northern sky
Sees danger's pennants flying
In clouds low lying.

Labouring through storm and spray
What hope have they ?
The Bar seethes white,
Vain shines the Harbour light,
Port after stormy seas
Is not for these.

                    D.M.W.
                     1933.

CHAPTER II

LINES AT CHRISTMAS

THE *Helena* was laid up, and I had been "Long Lining" in a trim coble called the *City of Leeds*. It was run by a man who had fetched his wife from Leeds and named the boat in her honour. Six keel-boats (40 to 50-foot boats decked in, and owning wheelhouses), had left the harbour. Lights glowed here and there, and voices carried across the water. From the narrow cobbled alleys, jerseyed figures ladened with skeps of baited lines, passed beneath the sparsely distributed street lamps, to be swallowed up in the shadow of the Fish Market. One after another the cobles started up their various engines, which coughed and spluttered, and finally chug-chugged out of the harbour, bound for the Inshore grounds. The crews were "tiding" their lines, shooting in on the ebb, to come out again and haul on the flood in a few hours' time. For this type of fishing mussels are the usual bait in winter.

Dawn revealed the Abbey etched black against snow-covered moors. The cox handed me the tiller and pointed to the old compass at his feet. "Steer East by North for twenty minutes from the Bell Buoy," he advised. It was as well to steer by the compass. In ten minutes a snow blizzard had completely hidden the land. The sea was "lipping and choughing," throwing showers of ice-cold spray into gaps between muffler and oilskin, to trickle maliciously down our necks. Over went the "ender," then 60 fathoms of tow line attached to the anchor, and the four lines, each with 360 hooks.

8

LOOKING OUT FOR THE BUOY
Will Storr, J. J. Storr, R. Harland

SHOOTING THE LINES

J. J. Storr (" Banger ") and R. Harland (" Deadeye ")

The second anchor, the end tow, and the second " ender " completed the gear, now safely stretched along the sea bottom, its position on the surface marked by the floating buoys.

Our gear over, we returned on the reverse course to port. The cold was intense. Leaning over the engine our silent engineer strove for a little warmth. He wore no oilskin in spite of the weather. His long, rather saturnine face was of a kind often seen aboard the King's ships. A tight mouth, with the grim corners danger and adversity are apt to bring. But it lightened into a surprising smile at sight of the two little girls waiting on the quay. One was his own, the other adopted, but it was obvious *he* belonged equally to both.

" Why did you adopt another girl ? " I once asked him, knowing the value of boys to a fisherman. " Lived down our street, mother died, girls want a home." It was a long speech for him. The cox's little grandson was with the two children, and with a crow of delight, he climbed to his grandad's shoulders. The old man supported a widowed daughter who could claim neither dole nor pension, her husband having worked on a share basis in the coble, a position holding at that time no unemployment insurance. He had accidentally walked over the quayside on a dark slippery morning : It had been a tragic case.

Her father was now the widow's main support. Re-shouldering the chief bread-winner's burden, he had again bent his neck to the yoke of the sea. " I'se always up first in a morning," he told me ; " I makes a dish of tea, and goes down the pier about 4 o'clock to look at the sea. I'se good health except for the quinsy." " Quinsy ? " I queried. " Yes, yes," he said, " most every winter." He added ruminatively, " But last

week I burst him with a hot potato!" We parted
to go our separate ways to breakfast, and, after a brief
spell ashore, went back to the lines.

The haul was fair, but the price at the auction very
low. I looked round and saw a study in "poker
faces." My hands had been too cold to unfasten my
oilskin in the boat, and I had been obliged to come
ashore in it. Now, as my numb fingers thawed a little,
I took it off, and wondered how long it would take me
to become a fatalist in this game with the sea. At the
close of that poor sale, the old man gave me a quick
look and took my coat, " Come and have a look at our
'mistletoe,'" he said, " I'se got it all ready for Christmas."

The little cottage was clean, and a bright fire glowed
a welcome. Hanging from a beam I saw a white paper
wreath decorated with tinsel and small toys. Lost in
antiquity, this custom of the ' Mistletoe' is preferred
here to the later one of the Christmas tree. The daughter,
her baby in her arms, pointed to it proudly. " Father's
done three this year," she said, " one for our Dave,
and another for those children whose mother died last
week. He's done them early as there are the wreaths
to make yet." A spasm of pain contracted her face.
Her father looked up quickly, " Show the lady the
tooth Ronny's been cutting," he told her. Maternal
pride swept the shadow from her eyes. The group
made a picture suggestive of Christmas; but it was in
the brave old eyes that I saw the vision of the Holy
Child. Out in the open, wind and sea had the sound
of trumpets. They blew for Him whose Hands still
tend the souls of men till they flower again into the
likeness of God.

> " Who abides in a terrible patience
>   Unangered, unworn,
> And again for the child that is squandered
>   A Child is born."   G.K.C.

HAULING THE LINES ON *PILOT ME*

COMRADES AND GUIDE ME AT THE QUAYSIDE

facing page 11]

The early walk down the pier mentioned by old Bob Harland was part of the day's ritual. One gloomy morning, two of our veteran skippers stood at the extension end watching the dark swell gleam in the revolving rays from the lighthouse.

" Now John Robert ! " " Now Mat ! "

Two of the keel-boat crews were waiting for the result of their skipper's survey. A given signal, and both *Success* and *Pilot Me* showed signs of activity aboard. The rhythm of their engines roused cottagers close to the harbour side. " Who's gone out ? " " Only John Robert and Mat." " Then it won't be weather for us," and coble crews drifted from the shelter of the Fish Market back to their firesides.

The beat of the engines grew fainter and died.

A skipper's judgment ! What depends on it ?

The livelihood of four or five families, the lives of as many men. The precious gear and crafts that, with the skill of their hands and the genius of their seamanship, compose these men's whole capital. The procuring of food for the many. Few skippers set out without consulting wireless and weather forecasts ; certainly ours did not, but not even these can foretell the exact time when the mood of the sea may change. Sometimes there is gear to be recovered after a warning has been received. So it happened on that day. The sea increased as time wore on, by 12 o'clock the gale, that rattled the townsmen's windows far inland, had lashed the northern sea to fury. The bar between the pier extensions had become impassable, sandbanks lying in the fairway, while the pros and cons of dredging were being discussed—made barriers of death. Even the lifeboat could not pass out as the tide fell. Still the boats had not returned. When they did, " Burn them off," rose the cry, denoting the old custom of lighting a fire on the pier end to warn incoming boats away from peril.

Swept by the giant seas, the men in the keel-boats accepted the verdict of those ashore, " To enter is death." Down below decks the crews realised the meaning of the revolving wheel and heeling craft. What next ? Twenty miles to the northward lay the nearest hope, twenty miles with every minute and every cable length fraught with death.

In the wheelhouse of the leading boat was Skipper Storr, D.S.M. He had served as an R.N.R. officer in " Q " boat and mine-sweeper in the Great War, and was widely appreciated as a Fishing Skipper of proved ability, but best known by all as a great Christian and devoted servant of his Church. Now faith, long experience, and steady hands on the wheel kept chaos at bay within and without. The men below did their share too, and engine room and forecastle were free from panic. Both crews—for the second boat, *Success*, had followed the lead of the first—knew that if lives are ever in the hands of men, theirs were in the hands of two of the finest seamen on the North-East Coast. So also knew the watchers in the home port. But they could see the size of the seas and the smallness of the two dwindling craft, dwindling amid the mirk and smother until nothing could any longer be seen but that.

The heavy day wore on. What dread tidings would come from that distant port ? None for long hours. But at last the awaited message came, " Both boats safe."

The epic of their entry into Hartlepool was in many papers. The story rang with the gallantry of the local lifeboat men, and deep commendation of our skipper's seamanship. There had been a few light casualities and much exhaustion.

PILOT ME COMES HOME WITH FISH

THE SINISTER BAR

"CODLING" IN THE *GOOD FAITH*

THE LIFEBOAT STANDS BY *FLYING SPRAY*

But, sipping their coffee, in dry clothes, with the
knowledge that their catch had sold unusually well,
and that their ships only needed a break in the weather
to return home, the brother skippers eyed each other
in thankful content.

CHAPTER III

THE *GOOD FAITH* (WY. 97)

THE launching of the *Good Faith* was a minor incident in the affairs of the town, but a tremendous event to me. She was locally built by Frank Clarkson and designed like the big Northumberland cobles I had seen at the Farne Islands. It was my plan to half-deck her, to protect the engine from the seas, and to have a long rudder affixed to a rod that could be raised or lowered in shallow or deep water. For the first year she had a petrol engine, but the prospect of having to renew the machinery frequently—which follows inevitably in boats, as it does in cars which use petrol—caused me to change it the second year for an Ailsa-Craig diesel, made in a special light-weight alloy.

After twelve years' use that engine is still in excellent condition, but its greatest service came when petrol was no longer procurable. As a " diesel " the *Good Faith*, " fisherman," carried a war-time permit that the use of petrol would probably have made prohibitive. But few thought of war in 1933.

On February 16th, she took her trial run out to sea. There was a strong tide running and someone told me she would be a stormy petrel : the name stuck. She has proved a good sea boat in rough weather.

She had a few accidents to start with, though the first was less an accident than bad management. She ran out of petrol after an eighty-mile cruise, a mile and a half from home. Happily a passing fellow fisherman gave her half a can full to save her the ignominy of a tow. The tow came, however, later. With a rope

14

WHITBY FISHERMEN AT SANDSEND, 1933
(A party to celebrate the launch of the *Good Faith*)

GOOD FAITH ALMOST READY FOR SEA

THE *GOOD FAITH* BECOMES AN OLD STAGER
(L. Mirfield clearing lines)

firmly fixed in her propeller, she was obliged to signal
for assistance, which arrived in the shape of two salmon
boats racing each other for the prize. As the second
drew up with the first, its rowers stood up and de-
liberately struck at the oars of the advancing boat.
They broke off short! The air grew torrid round the
idly-drifting *Good Faith*, and in haste, I promised to
divide the award of the tow between the two, whichever
boat was able to assist me, and eventually the rope was
passed to the undamaged "salmoner." Both crews
were waiting when I left the *Good Faith* at her moorings.
After that I had a "hand hole" fixed over the propeller,
with a brass valve that could be unscrewed at sea.
Many times since has it given me cause for thankfulness,
and saved us from a tow; and many tows has the
Good Faith given for the very *lack* of that "hand hole"
in the boats that needed her assistance.

Tows are all in the day's work among fishing boats.
The fact of my having to pay for the first one, measures
the distance between then and now. A pleasure boat
will usually be charged for this service. Fishermen help
each other in the free masonry of their craft. My
proudest moment was when this recognition first
came to me. One of the keel-boats had engine trouble,
and the crew were unable to take their gear to sea.
The skipper, knocking at my cottage, asked me to do
him that service, while he remained to superintend the
repairs aboard his craft. I had been down with "flu"
and was considering staying ashore, but nothing could
have kept me from the sea after that. We worked the
gear and came in laden with fish. From that time I
was asked for help of that kind as often as anyone else.
There was one tragic day I remember above the others.
A Scarborough boat had been in overnight and gone
out to his gear in the morning. About eleven I saw

him returning, his flag at half-mast, having lost a man overboard. He had come back to report, leaving his gear at sea, and I offered to fetch it for him.

It was an unforgettable morning. The directions had not been over clear—a fact hardly to be wondered at. The sea had a heavy and oily swell, and the grey-packed clouds seemed to lie on the top of us : we were long in finding the buoy. When found, the gear was unaccountably heavy, and our combined effort could hardly haul the lines. Mirfield, my engineer at that time, spoke suddenly, " It's the corpse we've got, dead men follow steel." As if the words had freed it, the weight left the line, and piece by piece we hauled the rest in, the steel hooks mostly empty, till with all gear aboard we turned for port.

As we thankfully crossed the Bar we saw that the storm cone had gone up on the East Cliff Station. The gale came, and though for long after men looked for the body of the poor Scarborough fisherman they found no sign of it. The sea was secretive and yielded nothing. . . .

We had had rather a terrible winter. Two boats had foundered, miraculously without loss of life. We were all " potting " at the time the first one went. It had been a bad morning for everyone, and the *Mizpah* was an old boat unfit for the stress of the weather. Driving through heavy seas in the open bay, she had sprung a dangerous leak. No efforts at the pump could keep the water down, and while one man had lit flares to signal their distress, others had sought to rig a boom in the hope of keeping themselves afloat till rescue came ; for it had become obvious the boat was going to sink. Meanwhile the keel-boat *Galilee*, steaming to her pots further down, had been arrested by the sight of flares. What could be the matter ? Round she came, full steam ahead. Another and

HOLIDAYS, 1933

(J.E.W., D.M.W., J.W., R. Harland)

GALILEE BRINGS HOME THE *MIZPAH'S* CREW

THE *EASTER MORN* REPLACES THE LOST *FAITH*

another flare blazed up, and now the skipper of the *Galilee* saw the desperate case of his fellow fishermen. The engineer of the *Mizpah* wiped the sweat from his face as the water seethed and bubbled in the engine-room itself. It was not possible to steam any longer; all men were now on deck ready for the fatal plunge, but up came the *Galilee* just in time. Three minutes after the crew had left her, the *Mizpah* lifted up her stern and sank—a fearsome sight to all who love a ship.

Only three days later, the rescued became the rescuers. They were in a fine new keel-boat, the *Endeavour*, and steamed out of harbour a short while before the fishing mule *Faith* struck the sand bar and broke her back. No one aboard the *Faith* realised at once the gravity of what had happened. It was not the first time boats had struck the bar, and reeling from the shock, the ship continued her journey to sea. A few miles out, the murder stood revealed; the bar had killed her, and she was sinking fast. Her crew burnt all inflammable gear and the *Endeavour*, arrested, swung round, racing to the rescue. The lifeboat was launched, but the *Endeavour* reached the *Faith* first, and received her crew aboard. In full view of the town, in dumb protest against the sand silted at the harbour mouth, the *Faith* went down, a martyr in the cause of the dredger, which arrived at long last.

The skipper and crew of the sunken ship invested in another new keel-boat the *Easter Morn*. And with her, other clipper-sterned, diesel-engined keelers made their début at the quay. *Progress, Provider, Flying Spray,* the big cobles *Silver Line* and *Comrades*; a new fleet was building up, and new prosperity dawning on our horizon. The dredger improved the Bar, and, one among the rest, the *Good Faith* went out to her daily job, gradually becoming one of the old stagers.

c

CHAPTER IV

ONE WEEK IN THE YEAR

A COBLE'S LOG (WY. 97)

JANUARY 24TH, 1939. The usual mystery trawler had been reported working on the off-shore grounds, and a very fury of potmaking and mending had resulted in most of the keel boats starting lobstering sooner than usual. Two of the bigger cobles had followed suit, and only five boats were now left pursuing the normal January business of long lining. We, in the *Good Faith,* were among these last.

The storm-cone had been up a week, but westerly gales at this port come from the land. When the smoke blows down the harbour, it is possible to go to sea in a wind which, if blowing at the same strength from any other quarter of the compass, would oblige a fishing boat of our size to keep snug inside. To-day, however, we had been forced to turn back. The *Golden Gate* coming in with her lines unshot should have given us sufficient warning. She is a mule, decked like a keel-boat, though without a wheelhouse, and considerably larger than a coble. What she could not master, certainly we could not. But obstinacy would make the attempt. Foiled, with ice-cold seas breaking over us with every plunge of the boat's bows, I brought the *Good Faith's* head round for harbour. As we steamed in, the *Golden Gate's* crew fixed an ironic eye on our baited skeps. "Too much for you?" her skipper shouted. "Yes, there was," but I felt no shame as I looked at the relative size of the two boats. At 2 o'clock we tried and got clear of the land.

With the wind blowing the lines and a strong tide carrying them fast astern, it was not easy to get the gear overboard; but at last it was done, and the "ender," its gay flags set on a bundle of corks, floated safely astern. We took note of the "marks" before heading for home. A bunch of trees on the high land over the Abbey, and Bay Ness and Staithes Headland out to north and south, gave us our position.

JANUARY 25TH. A fine day dawned with a fair prospect, but from 7 to 8 a.m. we wrestled with a self-starter that would not start. When the combined efforts of both of us finally set the coble going, it was clear a new battery was indicated, and if we were wise we should not that day permit the engine to stop. To be towed in was an experience we did not covet. The outer line brought the most fish, and we decided to shoot further afield on the morrow. When, five miles from land, we took our bearings and said good-bye to the "ender" little did we guess the trick it was going to play on us.

JANUARY 26TH. At 6-30 next morning the skippers and crews of the small craft were gathered on the "Look Out." The South Cone was up and some of the keel-boats had been late in starting. First one and then another had turned back. "No weather" for them was certainly "No weather" for us. But our chances were not destroyed as soon as theirs, for we fished nearer in shore, and a lull before noon gave us time to make a dash to our fishing-grounds and still return early enough for the market. But that day it did not come. We watched the hardier members of our bigger brothers return in the late afternoon, and heard that even some of them had been obliged to leave their gear behind.

That day there was much argument on the quay about the time of closing the market, some urging an earlier and others a later hour. Finally, however, it was fixed for 5 o'clock, to the satisfaction of the skippers who roamed further afield.

JANUARY 27TH. If by next morning we had not obtained and fitted the new battery, and so got the engine running " like a sewing machine," it is possible we might have heeded the big coble *Silver Line,* whose skipper called out to us that the " sea was growing;" but the urge to look at our Ender was irresistible, and to " look " was to get hold of it. Mirfield, my engineer, grasped the flag-pole as the boat came alongside, and asked if we were going to try to haul.

" We'll try, if it gets no worse," I replied.

Once hauling, we forgot the " if."

Fortunately for us the boat lay in a good position, meeting the steadily increasing swell head on. It was a race against time and tide, with the sea as our opponent, one to be watched, dodged, and thwarted. The first line came aboard. I changed the full skep for an empty one, grasped the line which Mirfield disconnected from the one aboard, gaffed a large cod, and somehow held on to the tiller.

The haul proceeded, Mirfield, both hands busy with the gear, telling me what he required of the boat in the monotonous series of engine and helm orders that can only be described as " The Song of the Haul."

With the long pole tied to the gear-lever in one hand and the tiller in the other, I endeavoured to follow or anticipate his words. " Ahead and to it, to it a bit, all right, out of gear now." Another fish to gaff. Then, " Off it, hard over and off it. All right, out of gear now." At last another line was safely on board.

There was now only one more line in the water.

LAURENCE MIRFIELD DISAPPROVES OF THE CATCH
Dogfish !

[facing page 20

LAUNCH OF *SILVER LINE*
Cox : Mr. C. Eglon (" Grab ")

A big swell lifted the boat and broke hissing just beyond. Again came the orders, this time with an anxious note. " Ahead again, ahead and to it—what's that ? "

I had already thrown the engine out of gear, for the sudden jar betokened the most common of the awkward accidents that can befall a boat working fishing gear at sea, a rope had become entangled round the propeller. But what rope ? That was the question. For the line was leading away from the coble in the right direction. Only the " ender " which should have been to starboard, was nowhere in sight. Rapidly hauling, Mirfield drew up a double line and the evil became apparent. Someone had pulled our anchor up and, throwing it back, had fouled the tow, which now led under the boat. The " ender " was jammed in the propeller.

The long boathook over the stern utterly failed to dislodge the obstruction. We hauled the anchor, lifted it inboard and cut the tow line. In our coble there is a hand-hole over the propeller fitted with a brass valve. It is inside the stern locker. To get at this was imperative, but the door was locked, and by an evil chance to-day the key was missing. As if rejoicing in its advantage, an extra big sea broke close by. The boat with the rudder up was gradually slewing round and soon the seas would get us abeam. Hammer and chisel forced the staple that held the padlock and enabled us to attack the obstinate valve which no fingers unaided could have moved. At the moment of victory another sea broke ; and as the hand-hole below us spouted like a blowing whale simultaneously with the deluge from above, we were out of action for a minute or so. Then Mirfield's arm was down the hole, his voice anxiously exclaiming, " I can't find it, it isn't there ! "

My arm, being thinner, went down further, and I felt the rope between the shaft and the propeller.

One turn of the engine might bring it within reach. There was no alternative, so we tried the experiment, and it jumped into view. Mirfield cut away the rope that bound the corks while I grasped the flag-pole and drew the " ender " through the hole, closing the valve. Starting up, the engine gave us, literally, a breathless moment. Would it go ahead now? Yes, it was sound; and just in time the boat's head swung round to a vicious sea.

The depth of the set had become a daunting sight. With eyes, nose and mouth continually filled with salt water, the tiller became my whole concern. Mirfield set himself to the pump. Not far away, but visible only at intervals on the top of a sea, we glimpsed a white coble, and then two more. Someone else had been in trouble, and was being towed in. We heard afterwards that it was the *Guide Me*. A vicious sea had put her engine out of action and the *Ramleh* and *Comrades* had gone to her rescue. They were afterwards rewarded by the Royal National Lifeboat Institution for their labours. The tow rope parted twice and the *Guide Me's* stem-iron came out with the strain. It was fortunate for her that the other boats were near at hand. The black bowl that she had fastened in her rigging had not been recognised at first by the others as a distress signal, and the crew had known some anxious moments.

Safe at our moorings, we considered the chances of a shot next day. Unless a sharp frost put the sea down, however, no coble would get out in the morning.

JANUARY 28TH. The frost did its work during the winter night, making it possible to go to sea and put the gear over. Fog prevented our taking any bearings, however, and we worked out the position by dead reckoning. A keel-boat passed about mid-day on her way home, and her course showed that either she or we were well out in our reckoning. We decided to trust our own compass and, " sailing blind " back to our in-end, discovered that our faith was justified. The keel-boat had a faulty compass, as his skipper let us know later. We felt pleased with ourselves, but it was somewhat humiliating on the following day to be unable to find the " ender."

JANUARY 29TH. Again and again we returned to our in-end and worked out the course we had shot, but without success. The outer end of our line had vanished. We finally decided that a steamboat must have taken it, and went to the in-end to haul off against the tide. This always means a loss of fish, which the tide pulls off the hooks, and a greater danger of breaking gear, not to mention the more serious mishap of getting a rope round the propeller. While we were hauling, another coble, the *George,* bore down on us. The skipper told us that both his " enders " were gone, one taken by steamers and the other broken, leaving his lines adrift. At one point he believed he had crossed ours. If so, our hooks might pick his up, and we might draw his line to the surface. Stopping his engines, he stood by. But on the first two lines nothing appeared and, disheartened, he returned to the harbour. No sooner was he out of sight, however, than a dead weight on our line signified that we had hold of a " foreign body "—probably his gear. And so it proved. Fixing one of our " ends " to his lines and throwing it clear, we finished our haul and came in with our own fish and the good news for the *George.*

Several Grimsby drifters had arrived and in the language of the quay " Fish was rags." There was a buyer short in the auction market, which made it worse. Coming back from the sale, we felt that it was hardly worth while taking the trouble to bait and " shoot in.'

But habit prevailed. Grumbling, but faithful, every one of the cobles went out with their gear in the afternoon. Not one of them saw it again.

JANUARY 30TH. Friday's weather excluded the small line-fishing craft. One of the larger keel-boats, the *Provider,* only just in from a hard day, went out again in kindness of heart to move the crab-pots belonging to the coble *Ramleh* from dangerous shallows to the comparative safety of deep water. The skipper of another of the larger vessels, the *Flying Spray,* was angry because I did not tell him—before it was too late—that my lines were in peril. Such is the brotherhood of these hardy seamen of the North-East Coast of Britain. But no one could foresee the storm that was to come—least of all the three keel-boats that set off on the following morning. Their skippers were experienced, and, though the seas were very heavy when they started, the wind was still in the north-west. At 9 a.m. it came round to the north-east, blowing at gale force, while the sea began to "make" rapidly. Soon, to the eyes of anxious watchers, Sandsend Bay presented nothing but an expanse of broken water until the snow squalls hid from view even that wilderness of sea and foam.

The *Endeavour* was the first boat to appear, and she came in during a lull in the blizzard. It was 10-30 then, and the lifeboat went to the outer bar as Mr. Hutchinson, the skipper of the new craft, brought her, with fine seamanship, through the chaos of waters. Relief at her safety was overshadowed by fears for the other two. A young girl with streaming eyes staring out into the storm, broke into sudden hysteria.

" I won't look at it, I won't, I won't."

She turned and ran up the street, another woman following.

Photo by]   [*Doran Bros., Whitby*

"DANDY" BRINGS *PILOT ME* OVER THE OUTER BAR

SUCCESS CROSSES THE INNER BAR

PILOT ME ON THE DOGGER
1933—1937

After that, anxiety was voiceless, concentrated in straining eyes and silent prayer.

Surely, Browning, writing of the " elements' rage, the fiend voices that rave," must have visualised such a scene as this. A thousand fiends seemed to be exulting in the screaming wind and the dull roar of the monstrous incoming seas, which had in them all the terror of primitive rage, thirsting to destroy.

In face of it, hearts that had forgotten orthodox prayers, turned to the only mightier Power to save, and others, whose prayers had never faltered, leaned on that Force, as their bodies leaned against the wind. Time passed, with even greater agony for those on shore than for those struggling in the little ships amid mighty seas. At last the cry went up from the watchers on the look-out, " They're coming."

It was a fearsome sight to see those wavering masts appear and then disappear again for what seemed an eternity in the watery valleys. Not until they were close at hand could the whole ship at any time be observed, then suddenly the hull, at a fearful angle, became visible on the top of a sea, only to vanish completely.

Struck by a succession of terrific waves, the first ship reeled amid the maelstrom on the outer bar. The life-boat, now unable to pass outside, remained stationed just inside the harbour. Continuing over the perilous shoal the *Pilot Me* slowed down as a huge wave running beneath her broke just ahead. Then, as if awaking to hope, she seized the advantage of a moment's smooth and rushed to safety.

Her colleague, the *Success,* caught on the crest of a great roller, left stamped on the minds of the onlookers a picture of a hurtling craft, with her crew, in life jackets, still gripping the ropes that had held a drogue which had been swept away in that tumultuous second.

It was then that it became noticeable that the first of these two ships, the *Pilot Me,* had not proceeded up the harbour, but had turned round, and was standing by with the lifeboat, ready to assist in any rescue that might be necessary.

By the mercy of heaven, and the seamanship of the two skippers, all were safe.

The crowd ran down the pier to greet the crews, hilarious in its relief. More soberly the men who had been through the ordeal stepped ashore and collected their gear.

Not yet did the thought of forty lines at sea, most likely lost, and many hundreds of smashed crab-pots, begin to oppress our minds. Many of us felt that we had witnessed a miracle of salvation, making the cost to ourselves of that fury of destruction a very small thing.

COL. J. WALKER, D.S.O., HOOKS A TUNNY
8th September, 1934

PILOT ME COMES HOME WITH THE FLAG FLYING
8th September, 1934

[*facing page* 26

     THE CATCH! TUNNY 780 LBS.

CHAPTER V

TUNNYING

When fishing for tunny had become a fashionable sport, and rules had been laid down for the ritual of its capture by rod and line, it was disconcerting to the experts to have the keel-boat *Pilot Me* coming in with one of the largest of these fish caught on a hand line, and the prospect of tunnying becoming a commercial proposition looming large ahead ! Correspondence waxed hot in the papers, while the *Pilot Me* went out again and caught another and another. I had the great luck to go out with him and see how it was done.

It was not the kind of weather in which it would have been possible to angle from a little rowing-boat. The *Pilot Me* rolled her bulwarks under ; Whitby High Light, friendly and flashing, faded astern ; the mast reeled and wheeled among the stars—the " Great Bear " ever ahead. We were making for the Dogger, east by north, a hundred and fifty mile trip, and the skipper let me take the wheel. As we ran on through the darkness, the floor of the sea appeared to be sloping downhill, a curious optical illusion I have often noticed at night. The herring fleet seemed to be coming up to us—whereas, actually, they had their nets down as we went by them. The dark hours passed, and in the faint light of dawn another light glimmered ; a trawler, her decks illuminated, was hauling her gear. We sent a cry across the water, " Any tunnee to-day," and heard the never-to-be-forgotten answer, " Plentee tunnee here." For it is round a trawler or drifter, hauling her gear, that the giant fish come to the surface to rush for the small fry that drop from the rising net.

At a later date, when my brother brought his small Flemish Pram dinghy and his huge rod, we would then have hastened to launch it, and hey for the bobbing float and the bending rod and the little boat towed about the seas by the furious fighting fish. But this time there was no dinghy aboard, and our preparations were of a different kind. Fish were thrown overboard in showers, and among them a herring secured with cotton to a hook and tackle attached to a line, the slack of which was ready coiled in baskets, with the end fastened to a large bladder. This in turn was attached by another fifty fathoms of line to a buoy. I was warned to stand clear of the tackle—no idle warning, for the fish struck, there was a sudden tightening, and the line hurtled overboard at amazing speed! Not till the mullock (or bladder) had bounded into the sea and given the fish its first check could anyone obtain a hold. We could have let the rest of the line run out and allowed the buoy to follow the mullock, but we did not. Obtaining a grip behind the first obstacle, we began a struggle that only ended when we brought our exhausted quarry to the side of the ship, to await the pulley that would lift him aboard. An astonishing monster he looked—780 lbs. of gleaming silver—for he was not black-backed like most of these fish. We feasted our eyes during the long trip back to port, arriving in the evening with the flag flying.

In three seasons of tunnying, two incidents stand out most vividly. One was on a day when we had sighted no tunny, though the *Pilot Me* had roamed the Dogger from dawn until the afternoon. We had met trawlers in plenty, one had supplied us with breakfast and four baskets of fresh herrings to take back to the town. We

RALPH STORR THROWS THE BAITED HOOK

8th September, 1934

FISH ALONGSIDE!

WE WATCH A HERRING TRAWLER WORK HIS GEAR

facing page 29]

had seen another one—not a herring fisher, with a "floating bag," a trawl beside him so full of fish that it had floated to the surface! We had caught a shark! But the monotony of utterance, "No tunnee to-day," had made our hearts afraid. Then suddenly, a long way off, we glimpsed what appeared to be the biggest tunnies we had seen yet. Steaming ahead, we came upon the strangest sight the "Dogger" had revealed, for the fish before us were not tunnies, but whales, and they were rolling in reckless haste, not after the shoal of cod that fled before them, but away from something that pursued after both. As our small boat, towing behind the *Pilot Me,* was lifted high on the back of one of the fleeing whales, we sighted the pursuer. Not all of him; some sinuous coils, a black and white back—or was it a head?—a horn! For that five-foot solid sharp-pointed protuberance could hardly be a *fin.* My camera clicked madly; thirty feet of him at least we saw, and as the amazing chase went by astern, we gazed wildly at each other for confirmation. "Did you see that?" "What was it?" Not even the South Kensington Natural History Museum, to whom I sent the photographs, could be quite sure. They diagnosed "A giant killer whale with a deformed dorsal fin"—perhaps—!

The second incident had no such vague conclusion. We were eating melons, throwing the rind astern, when Will Storr, the ship's engineer, pointed to our wake. "What's that?" he queried. As he spoke a large tunny leapt into full view, intent on the melon rind. It had been a "hand line day" owing to the heavy weather, and the skipper suggested that we might tempt the tunny to follow us into smoother seas nearer the land and enable my brother to use his rod and line in the small dinghy. So we continued throwing the rind till the swells gradually lessened, and all the time the tunny came on. At last we launched the boat and almost immediately the fish struck. But alas ! the seas were still heavy, and as a large wave lifted the little boat, the double strain of fish and sea proved too much for the excellent " Hardy's " line. It parted, and our big fish and our big hopes went with it. But we had added this to our store of marine knowledge, as an indisputable fact. Fish eat fruit !

WE CAUGHT A SHARK
9th September 1933

THE MYSTERIOUS FISH
9th September, 1933

facing page 30

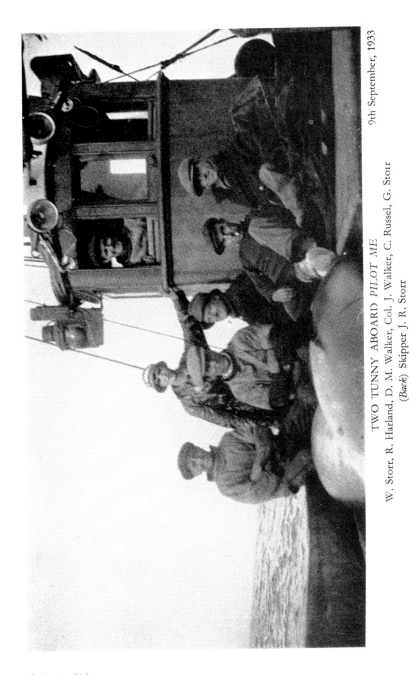

TWO TUNNY ABOARD *PILOT ME*

9th September, 1933

W. Storr, R. Harland, D. M. Walker, Col. J. Walker, C. Russel, G. Storr

(*Back*) Skipper J. R. Storr

TROUTING
(True Doggerel)

When dusk draws in and tides ebb out
We strive to net the tricky trout,
The dinghy dances on the tow
The engine kicks—and south we go.

At Saltwick, Graham's boat is laid,
At Whitestone our own course is stayed,
The engine stopped, the anchor down,
The Riding Light affixed and shown.

With ghostly yarn or choral song
We fill the hours of waiting long
Until, beneath the beetling cliff,
We start to work our nimble skiff.

With stones around, behind, before,
Avoided by the skilful oar,
The nets are shot with dext'rous zeal ;
Our fate is set for woe or weal.

Like bobbing heads with trailing hair
To right and left the weeds appear,
The corks—a sinuous dotted line—
The back rope of the nets define.

And next we turn our craft about
With " blashing " oar and echoing shout,
The startled fish rush out to sea
Into our nets—or so hope we !

We seize, we heave, we haul, we shout,
We wave on high a wriggling trout.
Ah, could we only catch his brother,
And then another and another.

The phosphorescent nets agleam
Fill ! and fulfil our wildest dream.
Toiling until the rising sun,
We count our catch—'tis thirty-one !

CHAPTER VI

TROUTING AND SALMONING

SUMMER visitors here see quite a lot of salmoning, but few of them see much of trouting. My own introduction to the one was through the other. I owned no salmon nets, and my dinghy was, in any case, too small for salmoning. I was therefore pleased when the redoubtable " Banger " Storr, skipper now of the fine new keel-boat *Provider,* asked me if I would like to take a turn at " Jazzing " in his salmon coble. " Jazzing " is quick shooting and hauling of nets in the path of the incoming salmon, which rush the river with the rising tide. I accepted with alacrity. It was one of those days on the edge of strong weather, when " Jazzing " at the pier end, and further on to the Rock, is most likely to be successful, if slightly hazardous. There were numerous cobles out. There is most swell on the Rock, but it is the best position, so thither our coble manœuvred. Just ahead of us was Mr. Leadley, skipper of *Success,* the most skilful salmon fisher in the Port. There was some rivalry between his and " Banger's " salmon coble at that time.

We rowed out to the Rock and began our Shot. The fish came in well. So busy were the men, that only I—occupied solely with baling out the considerable water the nets took in, saw the approaching breaker, and I had no time or power to do anything about it. " Banger " did everything possible, so that the huge sea broke just ahead, and not on top of us, nevertheless filling the coble, as it struck partly abeam, lifting it high in the air. I think we all expected to be in the water, but the nets over the other side prevented the boat capsizing.

With as yet only nine salmon aboard, it looked like returning to port, for three of our oars were broken, and all the thole-pins on one side ! So the nearest coble took our nets and lent us some oars to enable us to limp back to harbour—though not to stay. A carpenter mended the thole-pins, and in less than half an hour, with fresh oars, we rowed back to recover our nets and start again in the same position.

As if to make up for previous ill treatment, the sea was kind. In one haul we drew in eleven gleaming fish. Before the tide forced the last boat back to harbour we had netted thirty-four salmon—nine before the accident and twenty-five after. For that day at any rate " Banger's " was " Top Boat."

It was my engineer, Laurence Mirfield, who first suggested the *Good Faith* should invest in trout nets. They cost less than salmon nets, and our dinghy would quite well serve the purpose of a trout boat. He, Mirfield, was as experienced in catching trout as anyone in the port, and for a third hand—a necessity in this type of fishing—he could enlist the services of his brother George. So, the die being cast, I sent for the nets and purchased a licence to fish for salmon or trout in the sea. I was told that it was the first salmon-netting licence applied for or granted to a woman on this coast.

We set out about 9 o'clock in the evening in the *Good Faith*, towing the small trout boat the *Good Hope* full of the nets. Inshore trouting can only be attempted in smooth weather, and there was barely a ripple at the foot of the cliffs as we steamed past Saltwick and " High Whitby," the lighthouse showing a red gleam over Whitby Rock. All the way along the coast, cobles were

SHOOTING THE SALMON NETS

" JAZZING " HAULING THE NETS

[facing page 34

BREAKERS AHEAD!

WE NETTED ELEVEN FISH IN ONE HAUL

stationed in likely spots, though it was at least three hours before work could commence; and we realised that we should have to cross the Wyke at Robin Hood's Bay to find a clear ground, and start work under the great cliffs at Ravenscar.

Leaving the *Good Faith* securely anchored off shore, with her riding light as guide and beacon, we took the small *Good Hope* close in and commenced to shoot our nets in a semi-circle from the cliff base. George Mirfield, rowing, had to keep a good lookout for "Rooks" as they called the eddies above submerged rocks, but even so we had many an uncomfortable bump! During the first shot I had nothing to do— save to help George's lookout—but once that was over, my time was fully occupied baling and hauling. When we had shot the nets we rowed the boat back to its starting-point, "blashing" the water with the flat of the oars and rattling tin cans, and, after the first haul, baling the considerable amount of water the nets took in. As we startled the night with our clamour, the gulls added their quota to the noise, and the equally startled trout leaped from behind the stones where they were sleeping and sped for the open sea—into our nets! Back where we had started from, Mirfield and I commenced the haul, he pulling in the bottom leads of the net, while I grasped the floating corks. So we made a bag from which no prisoner could escape. Once the fish were disentangled from the mesh, we recommenced again— shoot, blash, haul and always bale. So up the coast nine times. Apart from the joy of the chase, which was considerable, the beauty of some of those nights would have been any artist's dream.

I have seen the net like a diamond shroud in the water, enveloping the silver fish, while the phosphorus dripped from the oars at every stroke. Above towered the cliffs, impenetrably black, till a great golden moon rose over the edge of them, illuminating everything.

Other nights were so full of stars that sea and sky intermingled, and we mistook the lights of the Scarborough herring fleet for a new constellation, and the *Good Faith's* riding light for another world. " There are a lot of ships anchored up there to-night," said Mirfield, staring at the sky. We had finished our last shot and were rowing back to our beacon star. Stiff and tired and very wet, we clambered aboard. I had a flask of cocoa, and sandwiches to restore our vigour, but it was even more renewed by the sight of the thirty-two trout reposing on the bottom boards of the *Good Hope*. As the dawn wind stirred, the *Good Faith* lifted her forefoot and set out for home. A successful night's work was over.

Two years of trouting made us feel " old hands," though 1939 was not a good year. Nevertheless, fishing up to Bay Ness and beyond it we had not done badly. But in July our " third hand " found work away, and for the time being another man was not procurable. So Mirfield and I decided to try trouting close to the harbour—on the Rock where in the salmon boat I had so nearly capsized. It would then be possible to work from our homes instead of from a parent ship, making shorter hours at sea. But we should be among the salmoners, using their method rather than our own, and this was our procedure. When shooting the net, Mirfield called to me to row straight on, then turn, making a " yook " that doubled the net back on to itself like a crochet hook. We did this an hour before the ebb, afterwards drifting and rowing near the net to take out any fish that rushed it. At ebb tide we hauled and re-shot the net again, turning the " yook " the other way. Rowing was hard work and I was glad when a friend of Mirfield's, a boy called Sparks, came and helped us once or twice. There were a few trout to be caught this way, but often when a fish rushed the net, it turned out to be a large horse mackerel ! August is the month of jelly fish and our hands were stung by them. As we sat waiting and watching, the red and green lights at the pier ends sprang into stronger prominence as the other lights went out ; voices of salmoners drifted across the water, " Plenty of blebs to-night "—splash ! as the jelly fish were thrown back into the sea. " Get the iron up before the big flood bends." Then the chug-chug of a motor boat and cries as he got entangled with a salmon net ! More shouts as he freed himself and ran into another. He was a small yacht returning from a cruise.

Searchlights wheeled far out on the horizon. War clouds were gathering, but we still clung on to hope. " We shall not go to war," said Mirfield firmly. I had no answer, nor did he expect one. A yellow moon rose behind the Abbey, mounting into the sky and growing smaller and brighter as it rose.

Three and a half hours we waited by the nets. There were no trout that night. And next day Hitler's army attacked Poland. Peace-time fishing was over.

L. MIRFIELD PREPARING THE TROUT NETS

TOWING THE NETS ON A TROUTING NIGHT

1939—"THE GOOD FAITH GETS A TIN HAT"

PART TWO

A YEAR OF WAR
1939—1940

CONVOY

Have you seen sheep on some green Yorkshire wold
By their wise sheep dogs gathered to the fold?
I thought of them when, on the sea's highway,
I watched destroyers shepherd ships to-day.

Imagining these watchdogs of the brine
Nipping the heels of any out of line,
Nosing a stray one back, a slow one on,
Guiding and guarding, till the whole were gone
To their appointed harbours far or near,
Leaving the Fisher watching by his gear.

D.M.W.   January, 1940.

40

CHAPTER VII

FISHERMEN OF ENGLAND

WHEN war broke out we had nine keel-boats and twenty-two cobles working, not to mention the salmon boats. The skippers are still with us and the crews, scattered over the seven seas, are getting gradually " demobbed." But some have paid the price for the continued existence of our civilisation and the hopes we cling to of a better world.

In war the roll of honour is heaviest at first in sea-board towns, because the greater number of seamen and fishermen are in the R.N.R.

As it was in the last war, when our skippers were young men in the Navy and Mercantile Marine, so it happened in this.

On the quayside the immediate effect of the declaration of war was a shortage of men and a re-shuffling of crews. The war made changes in the fishing as well as taking the fishermen. It was the potting season and the cobles would normally have been crabbing. That is done by letting down a string of pots to lie on the sea bottom. Each end of the string has a tow-line of from thirty to sixty fathoms terminating on the surface in a floating flag-buoy that can be found and picked up the next day.

But with the war came the minesweepers which, had we left our pots all night as previously, would have cut away our floating buoys, leaving our gear adrift on the sea bottom. So we had to rely on the kind of fishing that could be done in the day-time, when we could stay

by our lines and watch the buoys.   This meant " tiding "
(shooting on one tide and hauling on the next) for the
particular fish that could be caught at that season in that
way.   It happened to be dog fish.

It was the first time " dogs " had had any sale in
Whitby, though our keel-boats had gone seasonally to
fish for them out of Grimsby.   They are queer fish of
the shark class, with a sting in the dorsal fin that is
highly poisonous.   In pre-war days we killed them and
threw them back in the sea for the pest they were,
taking bait and biting pieces out of the other fish on
the lines.   But now they became our immediate quarry
and we set out to hunt for them.

I was fishing in the *Good Faith*, having taken aboard
the crew of the big coble *Silver Line*.   Her skipper, Mr.
Eglon, was converting his engine from petrol to
paraffin, so was without a boat, and I, who had lost
my crew, was very glad to take them out to work their
gear aboard my coble.   They brought eight lines.

From our first day's fishing we came back with
twenty-eight stone of " dogs."

Sirens began early in our port.   The first sounded
as I was walking back from the station with Mrs.
Mirfield, the wife of my pre-war engineer, and her little
son.   We had been seeing " Mirfield " off to Lowestoft,
along with a crowd of other bluejackets—our once blue-
jerseyed fishermen.

As we left the station, the infernal machine brayed
our ears with its clamour, and our minds with its un-
believable implication.   But that implication grew
plainer at sea.   The first morning the haul led us across
the course of a convoy coming down with its two
destroyers.   There were only fourteen ships, but it
seemed a large number then.   I watched " Grab "
Eglon nonchalantly gaff a fish while a big grey steamer

ORDERS CAME THAT DINGHIES MUST BE CARRIED
(*PROGRESS*)

TWENTY-EIGHT STONE OF DOGS

[*facing page* 42

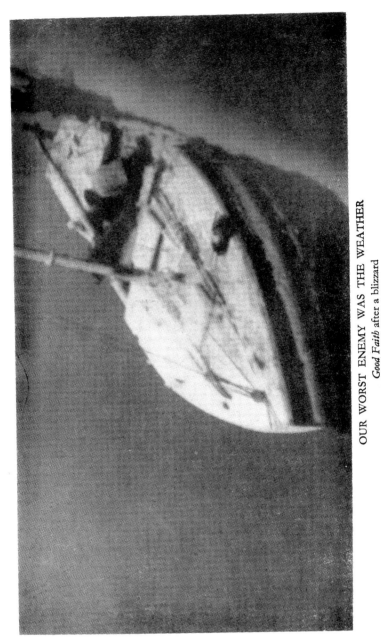

OUR WORST ENEMY WAS THE WEATHER
Good Faith after a blizzard

bore down on us; but his quick eyes had seen the altered helm as in true British style the big ships gave right of way to the small one intent on its job. The captain on the bridge returned our salutes, and the crew pointed to the fish but, alas, they would not have appreciated "dogs." The destroyer escort watched us through their binoculars, had done so from the first, for who knew then what might not be "suspect?" As they faded astern the sea looked very empty—but *was* it? That query held a sinister suggestion—as when the sea was strewn with wood after the torpedoing of a Finnish timber ship, or when Tom Wale, in the *Royal Empire,* brought in some ship's gear and four lifebelts. It was part of the day's work to look for salvage. The day the timber ship went down we had been late at sea, but after selling our fish we hurried out again to collect the wood, along with the other cobles, till it was too dark to see. It was also part of the day's work to look out for mines, and to begin with we did, owing to the novelty of the situation. After strong weather they were apt to come ashore and go off on the beaches. We were never sure whether the buoys, joined by a cable from the outer bar to Sandsend Ness, carried a net to trap mines, or to prevent the enemy landing. It was a great nuisance, as possessing only two openings it restricted our passage from "inside" to the offing, and *vice versa,* an inconvenience in bad weather. We heard of damage by mines at sea. A Scarborough boat whose gear the *Good Faith* had once retrieved, hit a mine going out in the early morning and was lost, with all hands.

We were coming home one afternoon in "jowly" weather, when the boat hit some submerged wreckage so hard the engine stopped with the jolt. There was nothing visible, and jokingly I suggested we had struck a mine and sunk it. But passing us on the Bar, Skipper Leadley, of *Success,* called out, " Did you see those eight mines floating to the south'ard ? " We saw one the next day. It was a red pear-shaped thing balanced on a ledge of rock where the ebb tide had left it, and loomed out of the fog as we hauled our gear towards it. " That's a mine," said old " Bill Tom," coiling the line on the nearby " skep." " Aye," retorted " Sambo " Eglon. " Grab " said nothing, giving the haul his undivided attention. I watched the sea splash round it. The tide was rising and it seemed to wobble. But the haul came to an end, and we went in and reported it to the coastguards. Someone from Bridlington came down to draw its sting. There was one mine the less.

Soon we began to see German aeroplanes. *Easter Morn* encountered one that circled him at mast height and then flew off. *Pilot Me* had a bomb dropped just ahead of him. Then came the brutal machine-gunning of a Scarborough skipper in his wheelhouse. And, shortly after, orders followed that the keel-boats must be armed. One by one the skippers went up for the old rifles that did duty for A.A. guns.

The *Good Faith* sported a revolver, but it was no use against the worst enemy we had to deal with—the weather ! The terrible severity of that winter of 1939-40 ! I kept a lamp burning in the engine room of my coble all night. With a diesel engine, using crude oil, I could safely do so. Cracked cylinders were a disastrous casualty, and they occurred in other cobles. Once the " dock end " was frozen so solid that boat-hooks failed to break the ice that held the cobles in. Bait froze and had to be melted with kettles full of hot water, and often, after a haul, the fish were fast to the bottom-boards in a sheet of ice.

Hauling in a grey and heaving sea, " Grab " Eglon

would cock his eye at the Eastern horizon and say,
" It's going to perform ! " And " perform " it did,
blizzards of hail and snow whipping up the sea till,
sometimes, when the wind veered into the north, gear
had to be cut or left at sea.

We were catching cod and skate and conger now,
the latter extremely lively. I saw one grip the gunwale
with its tail to throw itself overboard. We caught an
octopus that day. It wrapped its revolting tentacles
round Bill Tom's leg while he roared and stamped
himself free. Other tenuous sea creatures were on the
lines. Altogether it was an abhorrent catch !

There were a lot of wrecks that winter, and might
have been more, for we in our coble warned the hurrying
neutral ships more than once off the rocks. They kept
as close to England as they could. Unfortunately, they
sometimes went ashore. Then out came the lifeboat to
take off the crew and down went all the keel-boats to
help to salvage the wreck.

Once a Dutch boat aground off Sandsend Ness was
warped back into deep water by some of our keel-boats
—*Progress*, *Pilot Me*, *Provider* and *Success*. Then an armed
trawler ran on to the " Rock." Its hooting wakened me
about 3 a.m. and, getting up, I saw its red light and the
red and green lights of the keel-boats moving around it
in the fog and swell. The skippers tried to persuade the
captain to let them take his " kedge " into deep water.
He did not take their advice, and in the end the relentless
tide swept him further and further in till he ended up
close under the cliffs by the Spa ladder and there the
lifeboat had to come and take off all aboard. The ship
remained, strangely intact, close to the pier and the
harbour, though on the wrong side of safety, till the
north-east gales wrought their will on it.

A long interval passed between this wreck and the next.

CHAPTER VIII

" STORM "

BY this time, Eglon was in his own coble again, and I had procured the services of a man who had served in the last war and lost his hearing in an explosion. He was completely deaf, not even able to hear the guns, but I was lucky to get so good a seaman. I made out a small bundle of labels written with emergency orders. For ordinary times I had a slate, and we grew handy in the use of it. But one felt how much he had sacrificed of easy fellowship with other men. There were others making sacrifices to-day. The young lads who used to dig for sand-worms, to get us our bait, and carry fish when we came in with our catch, were all volunteering for the Royal and Merchant Navies.

Before they went, I gave a party to a group. Walter Hall, " Bella " Batch, Bobbie and Ronnie Noble, " Basser " Winspear and Joey Wood. We had ham and eggs for tea and afterwards put on gramophone records. I had a great number of these and left the boys to make their own choice. The most popular were " Fishermen of England " and Clara Butt's " Abide with me." I had a feeling that the local missioner would have been rather astonished at the latter choice!

" Bella " had made two efforts to join up; the first time he had been rejected on account of his teeth, and it had nearly broken his heart. " Get them all out then," he was told, " if you are so keen to go." And " Bella " *went*. He is still " somewhere at sea."

"SALTWICK NAB" WHERE THE BELGIAN STEAMER *CHARLES* WAS WRECKED

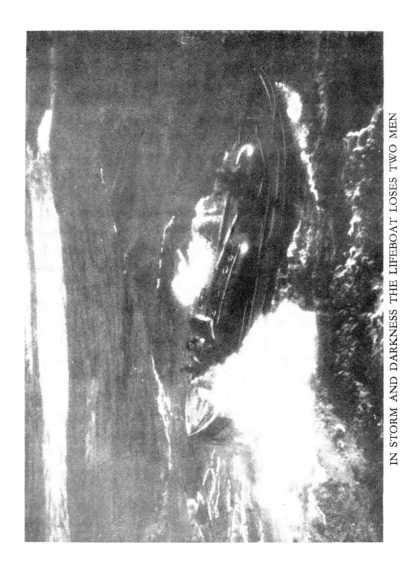

IN STORM AND DARKNESS THE LIFEBOAT LOSES TWO MEN

In February, 1940, the Belgian steamer *Charles* ran on the rocks off Saltwick Nab. It was the culmination of an exhausting and exciting day—one of those days beginning with an argument under the fish market as to whether it was worth while going out or not. "Worth while" if gear could be got overboard with a reasonable chance of its recovery—otherwise not. It is not the coble but the gear that is considered on these doubtful days. One man decided to go—Tom Wale—so the *Good Faith* set her engine going and *Silver Line* passed her on the Bar and *Margaret* followed. Not all of them recovered their gear that day, and when the storm came there was little hope of ever getting it back. One of the keel-boats was very late coming in.

As the younger men joined up, the older men, short handed, stayed longer and longer hours at sea. If it fell dark and the boat was still missing, other of the "keels" went out to search for him—with anyone aboard who chose to go; often the lifeboat went too. It was on the Bar that night at 7 o'clock when the last boat came in with the north-east wind behind him.

I had changed to a velvet frock and was sitting in a warm lamp-lit room, relaxed and resting, when at 9 o'clock the lifeboat signal went. My cottage door flew open and a woman, the daughter of old Joe Tomlinson—hero of many a score of rescues in his day—rushed in with the wind. "A steamer was aground off Saltwick! *Provider* and the lifeboat were going out to her." I had hopes of boarding *Provider*, but they were frustrated. A man fell from the top to the bottom of the "Crag" steps almost at my feet. It was impossible to tell how much he was hurt, and by the time we had telephoned the doctor and carried the man back home, both boats had gone. When for the second time I reached the black and snow-covered quay, they were coming in between the pier ends.

It was a bewildering moment, for not more than half an hour could have elapsed since they set off—no ime to effect a rescue. As the lifeboat bumped the landing, the cox stumbled ashore, supported by two men ; he was obviously badly injured. It was too dark to see anyone's face outside the light of one's torch, but—where *were* the others ? A hand touched my arm ; it was the fish auctioneer's. " There has been a terrible accident, Miss Walker," he said, " two men have been swept overboard, Mr. Dryden of *Prosperity* and little ' Kit ' Wale ; no one else knows yet." But a cry in the darkness revealed that the tragedy was out, and the bereaved relatives had discovered their loss.

Despite the horror and pity of the moment, my mind reverted to the ship, alone off that terrible shoal, and what might be happening to it. But others acted while I wondered. " Dandy " Storr, skipper of *Pilot Me,* with another volunteer crew, had obtained permission to take the lifeboat out again, and only a short time had elapsed before it was once more standing by the wreck. The coastguards signalled the steamer that it would remain there till morning, and as it was apparently impossible to get the men off in any other way, the rocket apparatus would then try a rescue with the " breeches buoy." All through the night of howling wind and driving snow, amid giant seas, the lifeboat stood by the ship. Only the comfort of its presence saved those men who still clung to the wreck from taking the hopeless step of trying to launch a raft to get ashore, which, alas, some of their crew had already done. Though no one knew it, their bodies were even then washing among the rocks with those of our lifeboat men.

I had put brandy and Oxo cubes in a first-aid box and set off to walk the three miles over the snow-covered cliffs to Saltwick. At the top I found two of our fishermen—" Stowaway Dryden " and " Pout Russell," both on leave—preparing a rope ladder for a descent.

" You are going down there ? " I queried.

" Yes," " Stow " answered. " The current will bring the bodies of our two men here if they wash up at all."

" They will not be alive."

" No, but we would like to get them."

I went on, leaving them to succeed in their brave work.

Another mile brought me to the Scaur. There was a way down, but it was a sheet of ice, and I found the cliffs themselves less difficult than the steps. The men at the bottom gave me a kindly welcome : there were sixteen all told—coastguards, fishermen, police and boys. The Ambulance was represented and all that was required out of my kit was the brandy and Oxo cubes. We broke in the door of a small tea shop and, lighting a huge fire, put water on to boil, to have all ready for the shipwrecked crew when they should come ashore. The Rocket Brigade had fixed the searchlight on the Nab and took turns to hold it steady, so that its light and the lifeboat's converged on the wreck. Once the seas, spouting a hundred feet above the broken funnel of the ship, blotted out the lifeboat's light and we thought it had been swamped, but it reappeared after what seemed an age of waiting. So heavy was the wind then that it was not possible to stand upright. Once we made a sally on to the rocks in a premature effort to get a rocket over. But it was not till nearly 6 o'clock that we succeeded. Sidling like crabs round to the front of the big Nab we prepared for action. It was my turn to hold the searchlight. The Rocket Brigade

E

fixed the tripod, and a rocket attached to a thin line shot skyward and sped over towards the wreck. But it fell short. Seven times we shot and hauled back the unsuccessful line. The relief of feeling the eighth tauten as the crew took hold was immense! Whip and Breeches Buoy were drawn over to the steamer, and with an indescribable thrill we watched the first survivor bobbing through the surf in response to our efforts on the rope. He was hurried to the warmth of the hut. Two—three—four, then, " There are no more! "

" No more ? "

" No, the others, they were on a raft, six of them, when we last saw them . . ."

The lifeboat, returning home, was signalled to go back and look for the raft.

It was not till over an hour later, when, stiff and cold, we finished the three-mile walk home and passed the fish pier, that we saw it coming in.

There was then nothing more that could be done.

CHAPTER IX

1940

THE clouds of war on the Continent deepened as the year 1940 advanced, and the snow-clouds over the North Sea changed to fog. Day after day it lay over the harbour like a pall. Through it we crept in and out of port, working by dead reckoning, while the Fish Company rang a bell on the extension end to direct us in. The bell was instituted after one day when some of us nearly failed to return. *Royal Empire* lost her way on the Rock and got among the breakers. The *Good Faith* almost foundered on " Upgang." It was a navigational error due to a miscalculation of speed. We turned south too late. The first indication of our mistake was a big grey comber running under us and breaking just ahead. We were loaded with pots and though I put the tiller hard down we were only half-way round when the next wave broke on top of us, knocking the pots off the deck and half filling the coble. Though head on to the third we took most of it aboard. There were only two fathoms when we sounded the lead. Visibility was " nil " and we could hear nothing but the sea. We sounded six fathoms and another coble loomed directly ahead. It was John Noble's. " Where are we ? " he called. " Upgang, I think," I shouted. Clear of the reef we put the anchor down and waited, hoping a homeward-bound keel-boat would give us our bearings, for which part of Upgang reef we had nearly foundered on we did not know. It was nearly an hour before the *Venus* appeared, and we crawled blindly in line till the extension piers reared up directly ahead and we knew we were at home.

Our next unpleasant experience in fog was five miles off shore, fishing at the back of the Navigation Buoy 19A, from which we often took shots out to sea.

Visibility was only a boat-length ahead when out of the wall of fog appeared a naval gunboat. He was coming straight for us and so close that my mind only remembered one sentence : " Safety lies in making for the Port Light." I swung the tiller to port—he towered over us, startled faces looking over the side. Then the fog swallowed him. His siren warned us others were at hand. There were three, emerging and disappearing one by one. The eerie wail of their sirens dying away in the distance followed us into port. This time we struck the Fairway in.

On another hazy morning on the way to the lines two " sweepers " came across our bows, and we saw what looked like one of our buoys possessed by the devil running for our stern. We had just time to recognise it for a part of the " sweep " and, by giving the boat all speed, to get clear in time.

Once a stray " paravane " gave us and several other cobles a busy half-hour. It had broken loose and lay in the Fairway, apparently a good piece of salvage to tow to port. But a broken wire attached to it and fast in the rocks beneath made it a most malignant tow and, after nearly stoving in the coble, we decided, as others had before us, to leave it alone ! A trawler picked it up later in the day. Commander Richardson was watching us through his binoculars with considerable mirth. He was our Fisheries Officer and as good a friend as any set of men could wish to have.

While we worked and others fought, the Germans took Norway, Holland, Belgium, France.

PROVIDER WENT OUT WITH THE LIFEBOAT

[*facing page* 52

[By permission of Kemsley Newspapers, Ltd.

JUNE, 1940—THE *GOOD FAITH* SET OUT AT 4·30 A.M.

One day I entered the Fish Company's offices and found Commander Richardson with the keel-boat skippers showing a chart to Skipper J. R. Storr. I had heard that the fleet of keels was to go south and from there across to help evacuate the B.E.F. from France.

"Are the cobles to go too?" I asked. "May we join?"

"If we need the cobles, you shall go," he said.

"They'll be wanted to fish in our stead," said Skipper Storr.

We watched the boats being provisioned.

They were to go at midnight. No one on the quay-side went to bed that night. But the awaited orders never came. I took the *Good Faith* out at dawn. It was a beautiful calm morning, so that our ground beyond 19A was farther out than usual. Two troop-ships went by laden with men. They were from the B.E.F.

We finished our haul and turned for home. Would our keel-boats be there? On the way in, a cat-fish among our catch seized a good-sized cod-fish and worried it like a dog. "Hawky" dropped it in a drum and put the cover on, grunting "Hun!"

And we found on our return that Dunkirk had "happened." The "hard and heavy tidings" Mr. Churchill had warned us of had been lightened by the glorious story of the little ships. If we had only been there!

The men expressed their feelings by playing football with the loaves of bread on the quay! It shocked the spectators but I understood. It was essential for some-one to kick something!

CHAPTER X

THEY LABOUR MIGHTILY

THERE was no bait! The whelks had failed to arrive. Something had to be done about it!

Skipper Storr, sitting on Tate Hill Pier, working at a net, had evidently solved the problem, for it turned out to be an eel net, and the following evening, shining in her new paint in the sunset light, the *Pilot Me* ran down the shore-side towing a little boat laden with the precious net. The shallows reached, the " tow " rowed in, and the men dragged the net, returning with shining cascades of little silver eels. There was a crowd on the quay as the boat came in. The trouble was, eel nets were not procurable. I heard a rumour that *Easter Morn* was lining the cod end of his trawl with a fine mesh and going sand-eeling with that. It might not be true! But " Hawky " and I had a beam trawl, and it seemed a workable idea to line the cod end with butter muslin from Woolworths and experiment with that!

The first trial was a success and the day after the quay *foamed* with butter muslin!

But we never did so well after the first day, and, along with other cobles, · fell into the habit of waiting for the eel boat, from which we never failed to receive a bucket or a half to supplement our catch.

They were strenuous days. Trawling early morning and evening, and baiting, shooting and hauling in between.

Every morning we went through the convoys at 4-30 a.m. There were no unescorted neutrals now, and

VENUS LED THE WAY THROUGH THE FOG

ENDEAVOUR WAS CALLED UP FIRST

WE HAD LEFT NOW ONLY A FLEET OF OPEN BOATS

EASTER MORN AND *PROSPERITY* RETURNED
AS PATROL BOATS

facing page 55]

their double lines would comprise some thirty or forty escorted ships.

Once these lines began to close up with the *Good Faith* in between! An escort ship was firing at a German 'plane. But before the dilemma became serious the big ships slowed down to let the little one through.

When sand-eeling finished, or failed through weather conditions, we went out and spun for mackerel. With these we caught turbot, haddock and whiting.

But war restrictions were shutting us in.

There was a boom across the harbour mouth that was lowered at sunset and not raised till the sun was up. This curtailed our hours at sea.

Next, our ships had to carry a white flag and show it coming in or going out of port. The selected colour of the flag was rather an offence. " Britain stands alone and will fight till victory is won " spoke our great Leader, and in his spirit we resented the white flag!

A Trinity boat was sent to watch our coast. True, it had our chief pilot—erstwhile coxwain of the *Helena*, Jack Douglas—as skipper and the patrol boats were manned by our own volunteers. But they were translated by their office and chased us when we failed to show our flag!

And then came the commandeering of the keel-boats. One after another they went. *Endeavour, Provider, Progress* and *Prosperity. Easter Morn, Venus, Galilee, Success.* Last of all, the old *Pilot Me.* She steamed out in the early morning—and the quay was empty indeed. Only the few cobles remained : *Comrades* and *Silver Line, Margaret, Brighter Hope,* the *Royal Empire,* the *Good Faith, Enterprize, June and Anne* and *Mayflower.* But we were not left alone for long.

The keel-boats were taken. But the veteran skippers were not retained despite their record and experience.

They returned to begin again in open cobles like our own, but larger. I had the honour to have the skippers of *Pilot Me* and *Success* working their gear aboard the *Good Faith* while waiting for their new craft. With thirteen lines, the buoys, the big dans and four men, the boat looked very full as I went to the engine. She was fuller still when she returned with the catch.

At the end of a week the new coble *Rosamond* arrived, and Skippers Leadley and Storr moved into her. The *Good Faith* took a crew of three boys under sixteen. A new coble came for *Progress's* skipper and another for *Easter Morn*—and others. Skipper Storr then brought the *Freda* from Bridlington and raised her bulwarks and had a small wheelhouse made. For a second winter of war was coming, and the country was going to need food. Though only open boats, they must carry the same quantity of gear.

For they were manned by the same indomitable men.

PART THREE

SHIPMATES

CHAPTER XI

FROM THE " SPARROW'S NEST "
(WILLIAM FORDON, Engineer *Good Faith*, 1934-37)

It was in February, 1934, that Will Fordon became engineer aboard my coble the *Good Faith*. He was a tall fellow with a lean clean build and a hawk face. The first thing I noted about him was speckless overalls and a clean white handkerchief. " A self-respecting man," I surmised, " and a bit of a dandy."

One of our first jobs was to go down to Skinningrove and pick up a small motor launch, the *Jolly Roger*, and tow it back to Whitby. It was badly in need of repairs, and my suggestion that Fordon should get aboard it to steer was very definitely turned down! I realized my engineer knew his own mind. It was strong weather and our tow-rope broke twice, but, though almost water-logged, the *Jolly Roger* finally came into Whitby Harbour in the *Good Faith's* wake on the end of the tow; and I think we were both glad to be rid of it.

Our next adventure was an encounter with a shoal of thresher sharks. In this case neither of us had any caution, and as I put all steam on and charged straight at them, Fordon lunged with the boat hook! He certainly hit the shark, and the next minute a welter of water came aboard as the great tail struck the sea near by. When the welter cleared they were well ahead—and, reason resuming its sway, we let them stay there. I suppose my instinct had been that of a hunter—Fordon's had commingled with it the seaman's ancient hatred for all sharks—the ocean's " fish of ill-omen."

I think his favourite fishing was lobstering. Going close in on a hot still day, creeping with the rudder up, with rocks to right and left, and fore and aft, to some pool known to him since boyhood and to his father before him, we dropped our thirty pots, and crept out again and into another pool to shoot the other twenty. We got some big lobsters those days, four in a pot sometimes, and some of them ancient grey-backs. Once, coming out, we found the tide had receded too far and my big rudder struck the " ground " ! Fordon examined it anxiously, but the damage was not visible. Only when within half a mile of port did disaster overtake us. With the sail up to help the engine, we were making excellent headway when, without warning, the tiller swung over to port, all pressure gone—and no wonder! Nothing but the rudder-head remained! Down came the sail and, with the sweeps overboard, we turned the coble round and, running the engine in stern gear, came into port steering with the oars !

We had one other catastrophe at sea that I remember. The coble had run to Scarborough, and the weather had deteriorated so much that local fishermen advised us not to venture back. Fordon agreed to the wisdom of the advice and shrugged his shoulders when I persisted in putting to sea, though making no comment. The wind was north, and heading into big seas the coble, despite all my efforts, occasionally crashed into the trough of a wave with a force that shook her from stem to stern. Came one fatal crash and the exhaust pipe broke, midway between the engine and the side of the boat ! We were about a third of the way home. " If we can prop it into position with boxes, etc., can you hold it together if you wrap your hands up ? " I asked Fordon. He answered promptly, " I can try." In the hectic two hours' run that followed, he knelt in the engine

room half smothered in escaping fumes, but keeping
the pipe in position, looking more like a Red Indian
than I had yet seen him.   Twice when the boat crashed
on a sea, the broken pipe came apart—but we made
Whitby Harbour at last.   "God's good!" Fordon said
as he got up.   "And we've done better than we
deserve!"   Those were very early days and, whatever
I thought then, I know now that I deserved the rebuke.
Those were also probation days for the *Good Faith*.
Whatever disapproval may have been felt on the quayside at the Institution of a woman fisherman, the brunt
of it came Fordon's way, not mine.   And he stayed by
his job three years, till the ship had won its position.
Somewhere else I have told how that happened.

If another ship was out of action, the *Good Faith* took
the gear and often her crew to sea.   These offers of help
were shrewd foresight on Fordon's part, though un-
thinking glad adventures on mine.   They won our way
into the Brotherhood of the Port.   The week when we
deputized for three keel-boats—the *Flying Spray,* the
Success and the *Provider,* we earned the entrée.   The day
when the *Pilot Me* sent a note in to say his hauling-gear
had broken down at sea, and that while he was working
his pots he would be glad if we would follow the
enclosed navigational instructions, and find and fetch in
his lines, marked our proudest achievement.   We found
the gear and brought it in after a difficult haul : the
Pilot Me was still at sea and the market nearly over.
After a brief hesitation I stepped in beside the fish
Fordon had brought ashore.   "We'd better sell it for
him," I said.   It sold well and, looking round, I met
appreciative grins.   In Fordon's was the most satisfaction.   That was 1936.

To-day, July 12th, 1945, coming ashore I encountered as hearty a smile of pleasure and a strong

handshake, and there was my old shipmate, back from
the wars, standing with his wife to watch the *Good Faith*
come in from some idle fishing.   As lean as ever and
twice as brown, in a smart check suit, my old engineer
gave me welcome.   " Come down and tell me where
you've been and what you've done," I asked him, and
the outcome of his story is the following yarn.   I believe
those who shared his experience, particularly in the early
days of the war, will like to have it, because the tie
between shipmates and their interest in their old ships
doesn't weaken with the years.

Lowestoft, 1939 !

Do you remember the " Sparrow's Nest," that
Variety Hall that was the clearing-station of R.N.R.
men ?   Coming from billets to the muster at 9 a.m.—
morning prayers with a hymn " For those at sea."   And
after the " dismissal " the gathering outside, where the
Naval Reserve Skippers picked their crews for minesweepers and patrol boats !   The drafting Master-at-
Arms and C.O. would shout out, " If any man wants
to volunteer with his friends or his family—father or
brother—they can all sail on the same ship ! "   But the
skippers, wanting men, cast keen eyes round for regular
seamen.   No greenhorns for them if they could help it !
Fordon was lucky.   Picked by James Bush, drifter
skipper and owner-master, of the big fishing trawler
St. Goran, he found himself obeying the command,
" Trawler crews fall in on the lawn ! " with twenty-one
good men.   This order was the daily routine, but there
came a morning at last when, " Well, boys, this is it—
we are going to Barrow-in-Furness ! " announced the
Skipper.

No one cheered, but everyone " took it on the chin."
This was their war—begun.   Despatched to the bedding
store for their two blankets—Yorkshire and Witney

WILL FORDEN BRINGS DOWN THE *GOOD FAITH*

WE TOWED IN THE *JOLLY ROGER*

THE CREW OF THE *MONIMIA*

ACTION STATIONS—*MONIMIA*

blankets—each man's own responsibility—they packed
their kit and got under weigh. The same evening they
left for Barrow-in-Furness. It took till the next evening
to reach it. Keen anxiety as to the nature of the ship
was in every heart. "Would she be fitted out for the
Admiralty, with wardroom and mess deck and the latest
improvements? Alas! The ship proved to be a fishing trawler just recruited after landing fish at Hull from
Iceland. The men stared in deep disappointment,
shared equally by the Skipper. But it was his duty to
cheer them. "We shall be aboard four or five months,
lads," he said, "but after that I can promise you we
shall take her into Liverpool to be converted into a
'man of war.'" Aboard they considered her armament.
She carried one twelve-pounder, two strip Lewis guns
and anti-submarine gear. There was no battery room
for her Asdic gear. This stood on planks which ran
through the ship's fish room. The set was on the top
bridge, and there was no chair for the two A.S. ratings
who, wearing the headphones, had perforce to stand for
their hour's watch before coming down to take their
trick at the wheel. The rest of the ship was equally
suggestive of a too rapid conversion from peace to war.

But such as she was, she must needs serve her
purpose. The next day, and for the following five, she
went out on trials. There were twenty-two men in the
trawler's crew. Eight "specials"—cox, gun layer,
chief engineer and second, two stokers and two A.S.
(Anti-Submarine) men. The rest were seamen whose
jobs Fordon described to be "deck work and steering."
Though, he said, in those early days the "specials"
also gave a hand with this.

The trawler's first job was to escort the cable ship,
the *Marie Louise McCay,* to the Southern Island, where
she was repairing the underseas cable. In fair weather

the job would have taken fifteen hours; but the dour Atlantic swell drove the cable ship back to port after only a brief attempt, while the trawler bucked and rolled on guard outside the " Skerries " for a week. At the end of that she went in to Swansea to coal, and afterwards was tossing in the swell for another week before the weather moderated sufficiently for the needs of the cable ship.

By this time Fordon had been landed, very ill, at a hospital in Valentia, where, when well enough to know anything, he found himself to be interned and not allowed beyond the precincts of the hospital grounds! This situation continued for nine weary weeks. At the end of that time, by agencies not to be revealed, he found himself in civilian clothes embarking on a small motor boat bound for the mainland. " It was a pity I didn't use my brains then," he soliloquized. " When I got back to my depot I found I had been reported ' dead.' I might never have been alive again during the war, if I hadn't gone and clamoured to be dug up."

His next post was to a minesweeper at Grimsby called the *Monimia*. She belonged to the Nineteenth Group and worked with the *Clovella,* the *Filey Bay* and the *Arkwright*. The latter was the flagship with the R.N.R. Lieut.-Commander on board. Her sweep was from Cromer to Flamborough Head.

As Fordon leant forward and lost himself in reminiscences, I also remembered! For morning after morning on the *Good Faith* on her way to the fishing grounds, I had seen the " sweepers," the long double lines of the convoys, faithfully escorted, following the cleared trail. But Fordon's narrative made a complete whole of only the part that I had seen.

The trawlers steamed abreast, two balls on the yard arm showing " sweeping in operation," the Oropesa

Sweep out astern in a half circle, the float in sight.   On the sweep wires, two fathoms down from the " kite," were the " cutters," like lobster claws, made to cut adrift the anchored mines.   As, severed from its base, a mine rose to the surface, the lookout on the trawler signalled to the flagship.   An immediate order was then given to one of the ships to take in his sweep and go and investigate the nationality of the mine.   Then came the command to explode it by rifle fire from three hundred yards' distance.   To do this it was necessary to hit any of the prongs, and in the frequent fog and swell this was no easy task.   Frequently the mine, full of bullet holes, sank, waterlogged, without exploding. " That probably meant one in a fisherman's nets some day," said Fordon ruefully.   But eight out of ten sunk that way in bad weather.   The *Monimia* had rather a good shooting record.   The skipper was keen as mustard, and so were the crew, though the blast of the explosion was terrific even at three hundred yards !

" Getting the sweep over was another ticklish job," he continued.   " If the Oropesa float was not in sight when 250 fathoms of sweep wire had run out, it meant that something had fouled and probably the kite had overturned and the chains were entangled.   Then the whole thing had to come in and be done over again. Sometimes a jerk on the ship would show that the sweep was foul of a wreck and the wire had parted.   Then the order would come to ' Knock out and haul in,' keeping a look-out in case a fouled mine should be drawn in under the ship.   When the broken tackle was aboard, the Oropesa and multiple kite had to be fetched separately, and very awkward things they were to get safely in.   But we used to do sixty or seventy miles a day," he said, " reaching Flamborough about 9 p.m. and anchoring for the night, and keeping watch and

F

watch. Then back to Sheringham. We never had a
sweep without a mine. Sometimes we shot at one for
four hours without exploding it, and had to end up by
going close to where we thought it was, to make sure
it was not floating waterlogged just below the surface."

The *Monimia* worked that sweep for six months.

One day, following storm and wrack, the four ships,
going out to clear the course of a south-bound convoy,
found the sea strewn with mines till, to quote Fordon,
" it looked like a turnip field! " After signalling the
convoy " Not to proceed," and seeing the escort close
up the line of merchantmen, as a sheep-dog gathers in
its flock, the trawlers hurried out to investigate. The
short day drew in, and darkness fell before the sweep
could begin. Other groups of trawlers had joined the
Nineteenth, and many ships were waiting in the dark
and dangerous waters. During the night tragedy befel.
Two trawlers, the *Manx Prince* and *Luda Lady* hit a
mine. But the first light of dawn saw the great sweep
start : the sinister field was cleared and the convoy went
on its way.

It was after this that night sweeping began.

The Port Minesweeping Officer—a R.N. Captain—
went to sea on the *Monimia* the first night, starting from
Cromer at 12 a.m. Two green lights took the place
of the two balls on the yard arm and another glowed on
the Oropesa. The men complained that the latter was
rather hard to see when the sweep was out. Nevertheless good sweeping was done and the night work greatly
helped the convoys. After five nights out, the *Monimia*
was relieved at 62.D. Buoy in the Humber for three days'
rest and one day's coaling and provisioning. The con-
cussion of exploding mines also necessitated some
repairs.

For six months she continued on her old ground,

then proceeded to Aberdeen to sweep between there and Rattery Head.

The good ship was moving towards her fate.

When first off Peterhead she dropped her propeller and had to be towed back to Aberdeen.

It was off Peterhead four months later that she met her doom. She was acting as " duty ship " on watch in the Bay all night. The weather was bad—the wind having risen to a full south-easterly gale. Anxiety regarding safe anchorage was increased by the sudden blacking out of all shore lights as the sirens went. The ship began to drag her anchor and, suddenly, to the pounding seas and bewildering blackness was added the hideous shock of the vessel striking and grinding on the rocks, where she remained hard and fast and partially submerged.

After sending distress signals, the crew crowded into the wheelhouse trying to pierce the blackness for signs of help. Their signal had been seen and the rocket apparatus was very quickly set up on Lido sands. Before long, rockets were dropping on either side of the ship and, at last, one struck true. The eager men pulled on the whip and the hawser, and secured it to the " gallows." The breeches buoy came over but alas ! it was evident that it was rigged too low, as the first two men to venture were dragged through the sea and almost drowned. Fordon, who was Leading Seaman, then volunteered to go up the mast and, with the help of two more men stationed half-way up, rigged a block, put the line through, and hauled the hawser to the yard arm. The ship's stern was lifting and crashing on the rocks, shaking the mast and funnels and making their efforts no mean feat. · But, at last, all necessary work was done and the breeches buoy was again in action. Then, when all but five of the crew were over, catastrophe befel. The whip broke on the shoreward side, leaving the buoy on the hawser stuck half-way between shore and ship. Happily, the line between the buoy and the ship was intact, and back came the man to the doubtful safety of the wreck.

At 7-30 in the morning the lifeboat came out but could not get alongside. But the light was growing and the five remaining members of the crew—clustered near the only warm spot, the top of the big boiler down inside the casing—came up to see the position of the ship—close under the cliffs beneath Crosse & Blackwell's jam factory! It looked possible that when the tide fell the men might get ashore in the Carley Float. It meant a long and weary wait, but it ended at last. The ship's papers were packed into Fordon's kitbag, the only dry one left, which with his usual forethought he had stowed under the whale-back in the port-side wash-house for safety. Then he and two other men with the precious bag got into the float and paddled ashore, Fordon returning alone for the C.O. and the cook, the last men on the ship.

They were all fed, rested, and cared-for in the Seamen's Mission.

Next day Fordon returned to the ship for the kit he had turned out of his bag when it was required for the ship's papers. He also brought back the " Bond "— the duty-free cigarettes, chocolates, etc.

There was the usual enquiry into the cause of the wreck.

Meanwhile, the crew were working by the ship under a Canadian Salvage Officer, La Page. The vessel was fast amidships, but lifted with the tides. Someone suggested packing her with empty barrels to give her more buoyancy, and six hundred of these were put inside her and the hatches sealed to wait the next big tide.

GUN PRACTICE

IN THE CARLEY FLOAT

[*facing page* 68

THE LORD HOTHAM

Only Fordon, fisherman, was gloomy as to the outcome. "Those barrels were new wood," he commented. Sure enough, at the next big tide she was deeper than before. And when the ends were knocked out of them the barrels proved to be two-thirds full of water! Over the side they went—all the six hundred!

The next venture was both more complicated and more dangerous. An old hulk was towed out and fastened with wire hawsers under the *Monimia's* counter, so that it would lift the stern when the tide rose. The ship might then come off the rock in the charge of the waiting tugs. The first tide was midnight and the tug *Attentive* started to pull. But the water was not yet high enough and the trawler was still hard and fast. But mid-day brought a great spring tide, and the old hulk under the ship's counter raised her so that the tugs could draw her off into deep water, amid rousing cheers. These changed their nature when it was perceived that the hulk beneath the ship's stern was pushing her head under water! Something had to be done and quickly, too.

The wire hawsers strapping the hulk in place must be chopped away, to enable the tug to draw it off so that the ship's stern could come down into the water again. "The Salvage Officer asked for volunteers," Fordon told me, "but there weren't any! No one wanted crushing like an egg shell between the two. It was a suicide job."

"What happened?" I asked.

"The Salvage Officer did it himself," Fordon replied. "He took an axe and got on the hulk, crawling around and chopping first one and then another of the wires. When he got to the last no one would look because we knew what would happen—but it didn't! Somehow he crawled between the two ships and finished

F2

the job, and before they crushed together he got back
again aboard. That fellow deserved the V.C. if ever
anyone did! The tugs drew the hulk away and took
the trawler to Peterhead, and then to Aberdeen, for big
repairs. That was the last we saw of her."

We got fourteen days' leave after that.

"What year have we got to now?" I enquired.

"It was November, 1942, when we were wrecked,"
Fordon replied. "I had a gunnery course at Chatham
after that and then was drafted to a motor fishing-boat,
Harmony. She didn't last long."

"Another wreck?" I queried.

"No. We were patrolling out of Inverness, three
days out, three in, and one morning at 1 a.m. we struck
a magnetic mine! There was no warning. We just
found ourselves in the water, holding on to any bits of
wreckage afloat. We were picked up at 4 a.m. by the
Lady of Man. All the crew—nine of us—were recovered.
I got fourteen days' survivor's leave after that. My next
ship was the *Arlatte*, a 'Double L' sweeper, all electric,
for magnetic mines. We worked her for seventeen
months with another ship, the *Sea King*, with a leave
every three months.

"Then I got a Foreign Service Draft. It was to
Milford Haven to join the *Lord Hotham*, a big armed
trawler. On Friday, the 29th July, 1943, we sailed to
'Gib.' and then to the trawler base.

"Our first job was to proceed to Madeira to pick up a
floating dock towed by two French tugs. One of them
was called the *Zuyder Zee*. We escorted it to Bizerta—a
run of 1,600 miles.

"Off Cape St. Vincent we got a 'ping' on the
hydrophones—a German submarine! We closed for
action stations. The senior ship, the *Imperialist*, com-
manded by Commander Craig Rogers, signalled to close

in and prepare to drop depth charges. We dropped
eight and the *Imperialist* four, but without seeing any
result, so proceeded on our course. We called in at
Algiers for water. There was a great convoy waiting
outside. We left again in the morning. It was very
slow going. The dock could only travel at four miles
per hour. We saw 'planes once, and the gun crews
stayed at action stations for three hours, but nothing
happened. We saw some rafts off a sunken merchant
ship another day—record of a submarine. The rafts
were empty of men but still provisioned. We took the
food and sank them. At last we left the dock at Bizerta."

The trawler then escorted two cargo boats to
"Boon," near Algiers, and next sailed for the Canary
Islands to pick up some Fleet Tenders and take them
to Casablanca. Afterwards the *Lord Hotham* did submarine patrols out in the Atlantic for six months, proceeding later to the Azores.

Fordon was meeting difficulties in this ship. The
old directions of "Port" and "Starboard" used in all
previous ones he had been in were now exchanged for
the words "Red" and "Green." And the R.N.R. men
commanding were very particular that all reports should
be given in the style and language of the Royal Navy.
The fisherman in Fordon found this very trying, particularly as in civilian life his officers had not been
seamen. A certain amount of friction was inevitable.

The trawler escorted ships from island to island in
the Azores. The weather was fine; there was plenty
of fresh fruit to eat; the war here was less evident.
But a call came to leave and proceed to "Puerta del
Guarda" to the assistance of a French aircraft carrier
that had been in collision with an American troopship.
The *Lord Hotham* conveyed five hundred American
troops from the troopship to the *Athlone Castle,* and

then escorted the aircraft carrier into the Atlantic, where she was taken out of the trawler's charge by two destroyers.

"We went back to the Azores afterwards," Fordon said, "and had fourteen days' rest. There were rumours of return to England, and while we were still wondering we were ordered back to Gibraltar, and in four days left for England. We put in at Falmouth, and there we were paid off and I took the first train home—and here I am!" he ended with a smile.

"That narrative," I told him, "deserves a draught of my best cider."

CHAPTER XII

THE MAGNETIC MINE

(Laurence Mirfield, Engineer *Good Faith*
1937—1939, rejoined 1945)

ON November 9th, 1937, Laurence Mirfield joined the
Good Faith, WY. 97, in the combined position of " chief "
and " mate." The coble was in luck's way.

A good engineer, he was also an excellent fisherman,
with a wide knowledge of how to work all the different
kinds of gear and a complete familiarity with the
" grounds."

Cheerful and competent, he was equally good in fair
weather or foul, and it was with a great sense of loss
that I saw him off at the outbreak of war. I had
accompanied his wife and child to the station and,
together with a crowd of friends and relatives, had
watched the train, with its load of R.N.R. men, out of sight.

To the North Sea and the Western Ocean, from the
Channel to the Pacific, to the Mediterranean and the
Far North—in every kind of ship our men were to serve.
Many were never to return.

But Mirfield was among those who came back to
his home, and it is the tale of his experiences which he
related to me that I am setting down here.

His train journey led him to that quondam Variety
Hall converted to a clearing for R.N.R. men, and known
as the " Sparrow's Nest." There, among men waiting
for a draft and skippers looking for crews, he remained
a week, till, on a Petty Officer's recommendation, he
volunteered for a ship known as *Portsmouth I.*

Picking a ship was rather like dipping in a bran tub for a sealed packet. It did not reveal itself at once. This one was already at Lowestoft, so there was a chance of seeing her soon, and, after collecting blankets and ship's stores, skipper and crew went down to the docks.

But what a disappointment they had!

Portsmouth I was the old wooden drifter *Dorienta.* Built in 1914, her accommodation was of the most primitive kind, and when the crew saw the sleeping conditions they one and all flatly refused to remain aboard.

The skipper, understanding their reluctance, granted leave to return to billets for that night, on condition all would join her at 6 a.m. next morning. He promised that the ship should be reconditioned on arrival at Portsmouth.

So, still grumbling, the crew boarded the drifter next day in the dark early morning, and she and her sister ship, *Portsmouth II,* later known as the *Golden Harvest,* slipped their moorings and made for the open sea. There was a strong north-easterly sea which soon sorted out the landsmen from the sailors.

Mirfield found himself one of a crew of thirteen men and appointed to the mate's watch.

There were two stokers, one " bunts " (signaller), the cook, and five seamen, besides the skipper, mate, and two engineers. The unlucky number thirteen was an additional cause for depression; but, had they only known it, the old wood hooker was to come through unscathed and not one of her crew fail to return.

On arrival at Portsmouth, after a rough passage, the skipper alone went ashore to discover " What next? " He returned to tell the crew they were to go to the barracks known as *H.M.S. Vernon* next day, as the ship was to be immediately reconditioned. The men were

LAURENCE MIRFIELD AND SON, 1939

[*facing page* 74

WHITBY R.N.R. MEN AT PORTSMOUTH

Back row : William Theaker, Robert Hansell, Fred Russel, Will Richardson

pleasantly surprised the next day when they saw the old *Dorienta* covered in with tarpaulins, so that, independent of the weather, the swarm of workmen now aboard could get busy as ants.

But it wasn't till the drifter, converted into a comfortable ship in four weeks' time, was moved to the jetty of *H.M.S. Vernon*, that the nature of her future work was revealed. She was to be one of the experimental ships attached to *H.M.S. Vernon*.

They loaded her with the experimental gear, wires, dans, kites, and some mysterious long bars covered with rubber. These, the men learned, were small magnets for shackling to the sweep wire. They were vital to the magnetic sweep, that was to counter the new magnetic mine the enemy had begun to drop in the estuaries and shallow water round the coast.

Mirfield went up with the rest of the crew to a lecture room in *H.M.S. Vernon*. "Now lads," began the lecturer, "you don't need lessons in seamanship—you are all fishermen or seamen, so I'll just tell you how to prepare and handle this new sweep." The men listened intently, and at 4 a.m. next day were aboard the drifter waiting for the " Big Bugs " they heard were to accompany them on the ship's first sweep.

In an expectant hush, covered by the dusk of the winter morning, the " Important People " came aboard, and the *Dorienta* and the *Golden Harvest,* the experimental sweep between, proceeded down the channel. But nothing happened and no mines were trapped. Twice, a third time the ships set out, and then the luck changed. They had swept diligently for some time when there was the roar and blast of an exploding mine and, alas, of the sweep wires too. The fault of the new experiment was revealed. It would be necessary to return to port after every mine destroyed, for at least two days' repairs to the sweep. Back went the drifter to *H.M.S. Vernon*, her foster parent. But in the latter some of the best brains of the country were at work, and a new experiment known as de-gauzing was later evolved. The two trawlers picked for this experiment had wires run all round the ship to demagnetise them and in this way they passed safely over the magnetic mines. All iron ships were afterwards fitted with that device.

But the mines had still to be demolished.

While Mirfield, aboard the *Dorienta,* saw larger magnets used and the same mishap occurring to the sweep on his ship, he met other men from other " foster ships " of *H.M.S. Vernon* and heard a different story. Something had been evolved which looked like defeating the magnetic mine ! The device was worked by two trawlers and called the " Double L " sweep. A long rubber-covered cable terminating in copper wires was uncoiled over the stern of the ship from a huge reel. This was connected to an electric generator on board. The electricity acted *through* the water and exploded any mine it passed over. Those two devices—the de-magnetising belt and the " Double L " sweep—dealt the death-blow to the magnetic mine.

But, while they were being perfected, the drifters continued to go out on their work of destruction, while the Germans, in response, reconstructed and altered the mines. To every new type they produced, *H.M.S. Vernon* and her working ships discovered and applied the antidote. And it was intriguing to realise that each success aboard the *Dorienta* or her sisters meant the installation of the new device in other ships. But failures spelt damage and, occasionally, accident. One fellow " townie " of Mirfield's had his thumb taken off by a wire.

One day, the third week in May, 1940, the ship had

been out doing her usual sweep and had not returned to port till midnight had struck. Those were long light nights and the weather had been fine. On arrival she had received a message to provision and coal ship immediately, and stand by for further orders ! Skipper and crew waited and wondered.

At 4 a.m. the following day word came through to proceed to sea to an unknown destination under sealed orders. In the mess deck the men chatted and wondered. Then a message was given to Mirfield to go to the skipper's cabin. Skipper and mate were together, looking grim and grave. "Well, Mirfield," the skipper told him, "we are going to Ramsgate for orders to proceed to Dunkirk to help to evacuate the B.E.F. ! "

The mate then went on deck to tell all hands. The men looked at each other. "That's bad," they said. But none of them knew how bad it was going to be.

The ship arrived at Ramsgate in fine weather. Crowding to the bulwarks, the men stared at the strange sight before them. In and around the harbour were ships of every description and hundreds of little boats, motor and rowing.

"What's it all about ? " the men asked each other. "What's happening over there ? "

They soon learned. All through the night convoys of ships passed them, outward and homeward bound, the bigger ships towing the small ones of lighter draught, and all the returning ships were packed with troops— the weary, mud-stained, blood-stained men from Dunkirk beaches.

The *Dorienta* had to wait some hours for the string of naval cutters she was to tow. When these arrived and were made fast to her stern, she joined the convoy leaving immediately for Dunkirk. And all the way over they were passed by ships of every kind going and returning, empty or laden with their precious cargo, and the men cheered each other, coming or going. Mirfield was at the wheel when the ship drew near to her target. "Do you see all that black smoke in the distance?" said the skipper, coming up. "That's where we have to go!" Shortly after, from the topmost bridge, he shouted an order to the gunners to stand by their only armament—two Lewis guns, as dive-bombers were attacking the convoy. Mirfield said his hands were ice-cold as he gripped the wheel, while the 'planes roared overhead and, through the racket, the skipper's voice sounded, coolly directing "*Hard a-port.*" They had a near miss and, shaken badly by bombs dropped both ahead and astern, the old hooker came nobly to her wheel, saved by correct judgment and immediate obedience.

The black smoke loomed closer, showing the glare of flame. Mustering the crew, the skipper told them that in a few minutes they would have to get into the small boats. He was going to take the wheel and run the ship as near on to the beach as he dared, as she was of shallow draught and the beach was of soft sand. "The nearer we can get in," he said, "the shorter distance the boats will have to go between the shore and the ship." This manœuvre would be a saving of life and time. Four men—Mirfield among them—each stepped into a boat and took charge of a string of boats behind.

Along the whole beach hundreds of others did the same. Soldiers were wading out and clambering aboard, and death was picking and choosing among them in an inferno of sound. . . .

"I don't think the crew thought of anything at the time except getting their boat-loads of troops back to safety," Mirfield said. "They relied on us." Miraculously the *Dorienta* escaped the bombs—and all her boat-loads were brought aboard. Again and again the men went back. Once Mirfield was startled by a hand on his shoulder and one of his "townies" got into his boat. The shore batteries struck near another one and wounded a soldier in the shoulder. And, at last, crammed with troops, the *Dorienta* churned back into deep water and turned for home. It was a light night and a never-to-be-forgotten scene. Masts and funnels of sunken ships showed in the shallow water near the beach. Sudden death struck from the dive-bombers and the shore batteries, and other ships plunged to join them. Full boats picked up more men, till it seemed they must sink under their load. And all the time they passed each other, coming and going, going and coming, the will of a Nation, undefeated in defeat.

As the *Dorienta* drew away, the men looked in each others' faces, scarred and marked by the ordeal, and hope rose in them. At Ramsgate the troops were disembarked and the R.N.R. men prepared to return. But Providence took a hand. The old wood ship had been badly shaken. Her engines needed repairing and the men were told that this work would take two days. During that period the Evacuation was completed. Dunkirk had become the historic symbol of Victory in Defeat.

Proceeding to Portsmouth, the *Dorienta* berthed at the jetty of H.M.S. *Vernon* to the sound of rousing cheers.

The Skipper was awarded the D.S.C.

It was after this that the air raids on England intensified, and crews of ships moored or docked round the coast found no rest ashore from the danger of their life afloat. The crew of the *Dorienta* were laughing and talking on the mess deck one Monday dinner-time, when one of the seamen walked in saying, " There goes the siren, lads ! " Custom, and their experiences at Dunkirk, had hardened them to danger, and they went on deck to watch the dockyard " maties " hurrying to the shelters as the atmosphere was filled with the pom-poms and A.A. fire from the ships. It was estimated that five hundred bombers took part in that raid.

" Very little damage was done to the dockyard," Mirfield said. " Our Fighters came in from every direction and the bombers soon made off." Yet those were Mr. Churchill's immortal " few "—for the Battle of Britain was on—and all through it the *Dorienta* and her sister ships continued their experimental sweeps.

There came a day when, arriving in at the usual time between 4 and 5 o'clock, and preparing to settle for the night, the crew heard the same old cry, " The siren's gone again." This time incendiaries showered down. The skipper gave orders to let go fore and aft, and proceed up the river away from the docks. When they dropped anchor, the men came on deck to stare at the panorama, where blazing buildings looked like torches in the night. When the shattering din was ended and a pall of smoke hung over all, the ship sailed back to her berth alongside the jetty—ready for the morning's sweep.

After the next big raid—March 10th, 1941—which did considerable damage to H.M.S. *Vernon* and her work-shops, the Experimental Base was moved north. Up followed her sweepers, and the old game of " pull Devil, pull Baker "—new mines, new sweeps, went on. The last time the old magnetic sweep was used Mirfield was at the wheel, and the Senior Officer came into the wheel-house for a chat, saying, " Well, Mirfield, this is the last time for the old sweep ; it *would* be remarkable if we blew a mine up." They put the sweep over shortly

THE CREW OF THE *DORIENTA*

THE *DORIENTA* SWEEPING

after and within five minutes the sweep blew a mine up—and itself with it! Hauling in what was left of the tackle the ship returned to port.

That was the last occasion she used the magnetic sweep. The kinds she tried were many and varied. Others, beside the magnetic, were: "The Oropesa"—a single-ship sweep with cutters on the wires like lobster claws to sever the cable of the anchored mine; the "Tail Sweep," which has no cutters but only small hooks or clips; the new "Explosive Cutter Sweep"—a two-ship sweep in which the cutters contained an explosive charge. The peculiar danger of this one lay in a pin that had to be drawn out of the cutter as the sweep went over the side. Carelessness could cause a premature explosion that could blow a man's hand off.

Mirfield had the unusual experience of remaining in one ship the whole of the war up to February, 1945.

Then, like a bolt from the blue, a "Relief" came up from Lowestoft, with the information that a change was to take place. Mirfield was standing on the deck when a sailor with a bag on his back came up, saying, "Is there a man called Mirfield aboard, because I'm the relief from Lowestoft he's to change with." Mirfield's expression elicitated the hurried remark, "It's not my fault, I've been sent here!" They sat together on a locker while Mirfield told the new hand what his work would be. Then, with the draft in his hand, he went down to the skipper. "Take a look at that!" he said. "No skylarking," said the skipper shortly—but a closer look proved the draft to be no joke. After his long service he was as sorry to lose Mirfield as Mirfield was to go.

But it was good-bye to the old *Dorienta* all the same. And good-bye to the magnetic mine!

But the Admiralty still had need of Mirfield; he was

sent out to Freetown in an armed merchantman as one of the crew to bring back H.M.T. *Holly*, which had been working with native ratings.

They called at Las Palmas, on the way back. "All the crew bought canaries" he told me. They were in cages singing like mad! The queer thing was that after they bought them the birds never sang again!

The war with Germany was over then, and on his arrival home Mirfield learned that his work with the Navy was over, too.

He came back in September, 1945, just six years after he had accompanied me on my first war-time cruise in the *Good Faith* to fetch a crab-pot hauler from Scarborough. We never met a ship that day, and heard later that a U-boat had also been cruising that area.

Next morning Mirfield's calling up papers came, and I lost my engineer.

To-day I again watched him coming up out of the coble, for Laurence Mirfield has rejoined the *Good Faith*.

" How's she running ? "   I asked.   " Running ? " he repeated, " *Why, that engine knew me !* "

BOSUN J. FLETCHER IN 1915
Mate of *Good Faith*, 1942-45

[*facing page* 82

MANNING THE LIFEBOAT IN 1900

THE LIFEBOAT GOES OUT TO-DAY, FEBRUARY, 1946

facing page 83]

LAST WORD

(February, 1946)

No more sirens, no more bombs, no more threat of sudden death from the skies. Only the war with the elements—the fight with the sea again!

The men in this book are still in that battle.

Many are back from the Seven Seas, starting work again in their fathers' ships or new ones of their own.

Some of these—*Victory Rose, Gem, Foxglove, North Star, Mona*—came in over the dread harbour bar to-day with the north-east wind behind them, the lifeboat standing by.

Pilot Me—still in grey war paint—came in on a run and turned round to stand by with the lifeboat.

For *Easter Morn*, caught in a smother of sea, had lost a man overboard, and young Robert Harland, fresh from the R.N.R., had dived out of the lifeboat into the whirlpool and caught the unconscious man. Harry Mirfield, at the wheel, turned the lifeboat with all the skill of his forefathers in his gripping hands. His crew laid hold of rescued and rescuer, and tragedy was averted.

Out at sea the keel-boat *Provider* sought to make the harbour.

"If he comes," said Harry Mirfield, "we must go out to him. If any man wants to get out, go now, for it's 100 to 1 we shan't get back." No one went.

But *Provider's* skipper saw the danger. No safe port here after stormy seas—but another twenty miles to go. He turned for Scarborough.

Baffled and raging, the sea swept three of his crew overboard, knocking the remaining two temporarily senseless. At fearful risk, " Banger " " broached " his craft. For he had seen two men in the water and turned to give them what protection he might. One had clung to a box, the other to an " ender." There was no sign of the third. Recovered from the sea's blows, the remaining two aboard rushed to assist. With rope and boathook, in deadly peril, all strove to get their shipmates in. By God's mercy they dragged them aboard.

Once more at the wheel, the skipper searched the surrounding seas, delaying till all hope of the third man's rescue was gone. Then, heavy-hearted, he made for Scarborough harbour and their last forlorn chance. There the lifeboat met them and both boats entered the port.

The father of the lost man told *Provider's* skipper, " No living man could have done more to save my son than you did at utmost risk to craft and crew."

The day's whole tale of peril and disaster would never have been told but for the Sinister Bar. The silted sand lying at the harbour mouth denies the boats a safe road in at certain states of wind and tide. Only continual vigilance and hard attack can overcome this ancient enemy. Great efforts are in progress. The dredger is working on it now—*Nil desperandum !*